THE RHETORIC OF SCIENCE

THE RHETORIC OF SCIENCE

A Methodological
Discussion of the Two-by-Two Table

BY

Roy G. Francis

THE UNIVERSITY OF MINNESOTA PRESS
Minneapolis

PUBLISHED IN GREAT BRITAIN, INDIA, AND PAKISTAN BY THE OXFORD UNIVERSITY PRESS
LONDON, BOMBAY, AND KARACHI, AND IN CANADA BY THOMAS ALLEN, LTD., TORONTO

PREFACE

The title of this volume reflects a point of view. Because of the intimate relation between operation and proof, I must admit that methodological considerations weigh heavily along with theoretical commitments. This in itself is an admission of bias. Although an empirical test of any proposition requires an operational contact with the world, I cannot share the extreme operationalist point of view, for four compelling reasons. First, I view tests of hypotheses as requiring a deductive logic which regards theory as logically prior to any data. Second, I admit inquiry—the process of developing hypotheses—as a part of science. Third, I am convinced that we can never have error-free measurement. This stems from my belief that a symbol derives its meaning from the interaction of those who share the symbol—and I cannot imagine perfect interaction. Finally, I look upon scientific activity as a creative activity. I refuse to countenance the notion that man is a passive agent waiting to be kicked by a stimulating world. Man, the scientist, recreates the world. He invents hypotheses. Logic can never dictate what premises a scientist ought to consider; it can only indicate that a particular argument is faulty.

The general outlines of the problem were of course the product of my undergraduate training, particularly my work with John M. Foskett at the University of Oregon. My debt to the late Thomas C. McCormick will be obvious, and the effect of my having studied under the late Howard Becker can also be noted. The Social Science Research Council, which supported my post-doctoral study of mathematics at Harvard, is largely responsible for my being able to clarify certain ideas. While I was at Harvard, Frederick Mosteller and the late Richard von Mises were particularly helpful.

Some of the ideas I express in this book have appeared in other forms. The relationship is not always direct, but readers of the *American Socio-*

logical *Review*, *Rural Sociology*, the *Midwest Sociologist*, and the *Alpha Kappa Deltan* will detect a familiarity with some of my earlier writings. Moreover, the ideas have been forged in the research mills of the Urban Life Research Institute at Tulane University, the University of Minnesota Agricultural Experiment Station, and Research Associates, a privately owned research agency.

It is almost unnecessary to point out my indebtedness to students. In particular, graduate students in sociology at the University of Minnesota have been very helpful. Although I shall mention but one, David Shaw, others have assisted in the ways students always assist the faculty in clarifying ideas. Mr. Shaw, however, called my attention to a paper on joint effects which was of inestimable value in effecting a modicum of closure. It is clearly unnecessary to point out the specific assistance given me by my colleagues. The fellowship granted me by the University of Minnesota Graduate School provided the opportunity to complete the manuscript. I must thank them; I do.

Finally, of course, I must acknowledge the assistance my wife and children gave me. Unlike some writers who must have absolute silence, I am able to stand distractions, provided they are at a minimum. My nine-year-old son and seven-year-old daughter were asleep when I did some of the writing; at other times (now, for example) they dropped in with some happy notion they wished to share. What my wife has put up with, only wives of other writers can possibly know. Her patience and encouragement, however, were precisely the things I needed most. And, happily, she has an uncanny knack for knowing when I need them badly.

Roy G. Francis

St. Paul, Minnesota

TABLE OF CONTENTS

THE RHETORIC OF SCIENCE

CHAPTER 1

Introduction

MAN is presumably aware of the world around him. He may not "know" the world; he may never know it. But whatever his reason, he makes statements about the world. Some of these statements are "true"; some are not. He may or may not have good reasons for offering whatever statements he does. Indeed, he may make "true" statements about the world, although the reasons are themselves "false."

Man is not only aware of the world around him. He lives "in" it. The world influences him, and helps to make him whatever he becomes. But that is not all: man influences the world. He does things to the world around him; he builds dams and floods fields, he builds fires, he builds engines. And, in building an engine, he takes into account the fact that moving parts become heated; he also makes allowance for the expansion of metal which accompanies heat. Man remembers the world. He has a past.

In having a past and in being aware of the world around him, man must live in the present. But his present is short-lived. One may raise all sorts of curious arguments as to how long the present actually is: how much time is consumed in the present? It may well be that man lives more in the future—if only an immediate future—than he does in the present. Be that as it may, it is certainly a matter of historical record that man, in the present, anticipates the future.

In his journey into the future, man is equipped only with what he, now, has gained from the past. Does the stuff he has accumulated in the past help him in the future? Under what conditions could the past help him? Apparently the world of the future must be similar to that of the past, or there would be no reason to expect past actions to guide future ones. Unless the event recur, one can scarcely learn from experience.

Man is not alone. There are others who are very much like him. They are a part of his world and he of theirs. From time to time, he has a desire to share his world with them. This he can do only if the others react similarly to a similar set of stimuli. Although he can share his world with others through the use of symbols, it must be understood that symbols derive their meaning from the behavior of men. As the behavior suggested by the symbol changes, the meaning changes. For example, a black leather jacket at one time connoted the ace of World War I—in general something heroic. Today, the black leather jacket connotes something akin to a juvenile delinquent. What has changed is not the symbol; nor will any machinations addressed to the symbol itself effect any important consequent. What has happened is that the symbol now induces a different set of behaviors, and hence has different meanings, than it did in a time gone by.

We say that man develops a system of symbols with which he communicates his *ideas* about the world. It must be made clear that man's ideas involve a conceptualization of the world itself (the world of fact), an explanation of this world, and a judgment of the world. That is to say, it is at least analytically possible to distinguish between statements of fact, their explanation, and these two from any judgment that may be offered. Of course, a person may prejudge a fact; he may *name* a fact in such a way that the response is one of value or mood rather than apprehension.

The possibility of invoking a judgment in the process of naming something in the world carries important implications. The most significant is that one may believe something to be true without having proper reasons for that belief. Although the fine line I draw may be quite arbitrary, I shall distinguish between things that are properly and improperly believed. The former I shall call *knowledge*; the latter I shall call *belief*. The distinction I offer is that knowledge flows from rules which we invoke to enable us to judge a statement as being proper or not. If the statement appeals to inadmissible rules, or is governed by no rules at all, I should assert that this statement is believed rather than known.

4

We are now able to state the problem: what kind of rules will we choose to have? The question seems simple enough. The answer will be very complex.

For one thing, we must distinguish among several different kinds of knowledge. At least, we are willing to admit that there are several different kinds of knowledge. Or, in particular, we do not wish to suppose that science is synonymous with knowledge. In our definition, science is known, but not all that is known is science.

We will concern ourselves in this volume with scientific knowledge. We need not define any other kind of knowledge. What is true of science may, in some respects, be also true of other belief systems. This does not mean that the characteristic in question is irrelevant to science. It must, however, be shown to be relevant to knowledge.

SCIENCE AS KNOWLEDGE

Awareness of the trap that man finds himself in—the gap between the past and the future—has led some to suspect that science is a technique for guessing the future. In the world of behavior, this is a reasonable use for knowledge, scientific or otherwise. As a matter of fact, much has been written on the superiority of science over other ways of knowing the future. Those who are addicted to this way of thinking tend to assert that the goal of science is prediction.

It may well be that such is the goal of some particular scientist, or, for that matter, all known scientists. The motivation of the scientist, however, need not be employed to describe science itself. As a matter of fact, those who would make science a bridge between the past and the future make an error. Although science may include statements that contain references to time, the supposed generality of science means that it is atemporal. And, as we shall see, the logic used in science is itself atemporal. The passage of time is a matter of the content, not the structure, of science.

Although, at some place, science makes contact with a knowable—and, essentially, a kickable—world, science is made up of statements about the world. These—like any other statements—may be true or false. To be known, the statements must flow from a set of rules. The goal of science is to develop a set of true statements (whatever that may mean; however that may be shown).

The kind of statements science seeks to develop are those that explain statements containing data. The explanatory statements assert relations; these relations we shall call principles. Then, if the relation is true, the data statement (the problematic statement) must also be true. When this condition exists, the problematic statement is explained. That is to say, the data are accounted for by some principle of relationship.

But science is not interested in merely cataloguing a set of statements. Not only are data statements related to principles, but principles are related among themselves. A body of principles thus related is called a theory. Now it must be understood that a theory contains not only statements of relation, but also the definitions of the terms employed in the statements.

The interesting things about the data statement, as distinct from the principle, is that it is rooted in time and space. Facts occur here and now. Principles are timeless; they exist now and then. The theory which explains at least some observations is "timeless" in the same sense that the principles are.

The issue may be restated. If the goal of science is a theory, what becomes of prediction? To understand the role of prediction, one must understand the nature of statements of relation,[1] and how these are related to the solution of problems.

We may assert that a problem exists whenever an explanation is wanting. One customarily observes some kind of behavior. He develops an explanation for it: "Because X is true, I must observe what I say I observe." The proposed solution is called a hypothesis; the hypothesis contains some kind of relation. Some writers have developed a style which suggests that any doubted statement is a hypothesis. I believe that such a formulation is useless; as a matter of fact, all propositions in science are doubted at one time or another. Merely doubting a proposition does not make it a hypothesis. As I shall use the term, a hypothesis is a proposition asserting a relationship which is proposed for test. In the most precise sciences, the relationship is in doubt. In the less precise sciences, one doubts the existence of the premise, the conclusion, or both. Only after a body of science becomes sophisticated does the relation between the premise and the conclusion become subject to test.

Be that as it may, a hypothesis customarily takes the form "If A, then B." But this is not a prediction. No commitment to this world is made. Only when one is able to assert the existence of the premise (A) is one able to *predict* the occurrence of the consequent (B). Hence a predictive statement involves an argument of the following sort: If A, then B; A—therefore B. Now, if B does materialize, one asserts that the hypothesis is verified; if B fails to occur, one asserts that the hypothesis is false. In the sloppy sciences, the doubt centers on A; in the precise sciences, the doubt centers on the then-ness of the asserted relationship.

In testing the correctness of a theory, a scientist employs the predictive statement. But he is not concerned solely with prediction, nor is prediction the only criterion of acceptability. Other criteria are admissible. Moreover, in denying that prediction is the goal of science, we avoid the trivial kinds of prediction which are always possible. Consider the possibility of measuring attitudes toward anything—say, toward the church. Assume that we know the attitudes of a number of people. What can be predicted from this? One can dream up a trivial prediction, nay, a trivial experiment. We will let the subjects (each of whom is measured with respect to his attitude toward the church) eat a bar of candy. We then measure their attitudes toward the church again. Could we predict the outcome? We would be able to predict with a narrow margin of error if the measuring instrument were reliable.

Clearly, this kind of prediction is pretty useless. So useless that we must deny that prediction is the *goal* of science. Prediction is a usable instrument in science. We must avoid this simple-minded interpretation of the goal of science. And we achieve this when we take the position I do, namely, that the goal of science is a theory.

We have mentioned one way to test theory, and have used symbolic representations that are more or less familiar. For this to be called knowledge, we need to develop a set of rules. This is the purpose of this volume. This is what methodology is all about.

SCIENCE AS BEHAVIOR

Science, though it can be abstracted from any particular human being, is a part of human culture. It is a kind of human behavior. As such, it occurs in a social situation. Not merely the social sciences, but all of the sciences occur in a social situation. The scientist is a marginal man; he emerges from a common-sense culture and partakes of a special one.[2] He variously accepts culturally defined goals and problems. He interacts with other scientists. He writes his reports. He submits them for editorial judgment. They are read by colleagues who judge these reports. He is variously rewarded for his behavior.

Whatever else he does as a scientist, he comes to a decision about propositions.[3] He must decide whether a statement is true and should be incorporated into science or is false and must be rejected. If a false statement is to be rejected, he may also seek to decide the truth value of an alternative statement. His errors are limited. He may accept a statement which is false, or he may reject a statement which is true. He must have rules which will enable him to minimize these errors, and rules to guide him in the decision-making process. He should pay more attention to the consequences of both kinds of error. Knowing the consequences, he may set a more realistic price on accepting either kind of error.

It must not be imagined that the rules for minimizing error are empirically determined. That is, one cannot use these rules to predict the behavior of the scientist. Why a particular scientist accepts a particular proposition (or even considers it, for that matter) is not merely a matter of methodology. It is as much a matter of the sociology of science which, like sociologies of anything else, seeks to explain human behavior. A person may include a certain statement merely because it is flattering to the editor who will judge an article for publication. He may include the statement because of a cultural bias. He may include it because it flows from his research design. Why he included this particular statement is an interesting contextual problem in the domain of sociology. We must not confuse the empirical question with the question of methodology.

Methodology, including the rules of the game, constitutes the moral code of scientific behavior. On the basis of an accepted body of rules, one may properly judge the quality of research done by others (or by himself). This is contrary to Lazarsfeld's position, which holds that a methodologist merely describes how scientists do behave, not how they ought to.[4] One difficulty with Lazarsfeld's position is that it can never allow for criticism of research; it provides no basis for judgment. It may be safer for one's reputation not to have his research design questioned. If research designs were not questioned advances in science could only follow from the establishment of great names upon whose personal approval new findings are accepted. This is conducive to the creation of intellectual empires. If his study is defined as good because a good man did it, a scientist may never feel called upon to communicate to others how he did the study. Failure of the lowly-rated scientist to replicate can be looked upon as a flaw in his work rather than as a challenge to the great man. Hence one allows for advances in science only if one rejects the idea that great names do great research.

Looking at the scientific act as human behavior which necessitates communication among scientists calls our attention to the substance of science—propositions about the real world. It forces one to recognize that propositions stand in logical relation to each other, partly as the terms are defined, and partly because of the fixed nature of the world of fact.

THE ROLE OF PROPOSITIONS IN SCIENCE

A proposition is a statement about the real world. Logically (as we shall see) it may be true or false. But, to the scientist, a proposition may have another truth value—it may be held in doubt. Although logic is atemporal, the resolution of doubt requires the passage of time.

It would be difficult to imagine science as illogical. Merely requiring scientific statements to be logically connected does not satisfy us much, unless there is only one kind of logical relation (actually, there is more than one). One must determine just what the relations are.

Knowledge of how propositions are related does not exhaust the use of logic. From the relationships one may establish various rules for judging other propositions. Thus, if one knows that A is true and that A and B are related in a particular way, he inferentially knows the truth value of B.

Formal characteristics of propositions (the form of the statements independent of their content) allow for logical structuring. From the form alone we may judge the correctness of the argument; from the form alone we may judge whether the conclusion was reached properly. But logic does not invent propositions; nor does it have anything to do with the content of the propositions.

One may have a formally correct argument and still assert nonsense about the real world. We must distinguish between formal and material fallacies. In order to determine whether a material fallacy has been committed, we must have rules connecting logical categories with the real world. We may have a proposition about the relation between geomorphic synoptical behavior and ostrological lackadoons, under conditions known to favor the existence of lackadoons. An immediate problem is: How can we test the asserted relation? As far as I know, this cannot be done, for the simple reason that the categories "geomorphic synoptical behavior" and "ostrological lackadoons" have no members in this world.

In order to test the asserted relations, the two categories must be shown to have members, and that membership must be assigned to these categories in terms of the conditions as stated. Some procedures for giving content to the logical form are needed. In general, in order that a relationship may be tested, a set of operational specifications is needed. Operational specifications are simply those procedures which identify this-world members of the logical categories involved in the argument. It is the operational specification which connects the concept to the world of fact. Unless such specifications are agreed upon, no limiting condition may be presented which will allow for the judgment of the falsity of a proposed statement.

I suggest careful attention to the terminology just employed. The term is *operational specification*, not *operational definition*, as is commonly used. I deny the possibility of defining anything by announcing a set of operations; the intent of definition is not contained in operations. This is simply an inadmissible idea. The idea of defining heat in terms of a thermometer is essentially a naive approach to operations. Basically, it begs the question: it assumes we know that we are measuring heat and not, say, height. A definition as normally conceived contains the distinction between such variables. Merely "knowing" that heat is not height does not save the day. A position which requires this knowledge without formal definition merely asserts that common sense is superior to scientific knowledge. Any proposition that serves to distinguish between heat and (to continue the trivial example) height serves also to define heat. Reading dials does not solve the problem. In the social sciences, the distinction is truly of immediate consequence. For example, it is impossible, from an analysis of the content of items in intelligence tests, to assert that learning or cultural experience is not as much measured as "intelligence." To define intelligence in terms of the proposed set of items and subsequent arithmetic manipulation is clearly to beg the question. All this would give us would be a summary of space-time-located information. This places too great a burden on generalization. We are forced to surrender any naive notion of defining things operationally. At the same time, I repeat the requirement of developing some operational specification of our conceptual scheme if propositions are to be tested.

The history of operationalism in the social sciences is replete with in-

INTRODUCTION

credible errors.[5] Although some theorists assert that social and natural sciences converge,[6] a subtle historical error is compounded in most arguments. Some sociologists have fawned on physics as a model. Many younger sociologists are in the mathematical-model-building business[7] and probably have some vague notion of mathematical physics in mind. And one may well expect this sort of imagery when we consider that most books on the calculus frequently use examples from physics. The error is in talking about a *convergence*; a forced attempt to copy from physics does not warrant an inference of convergence.

Moreover, what is often forgotten is that another intellectual predecessor of the social sciences often called a natural science is biology. One of the early problems of biology was the classification of species. Indeed, early books on scientific method named classification as the step which followed observation in the sequence of science. It was in borrowing from the taxonomic activities of biologists that many social sciences fell into sinful ways. Consider the task of the biologist when he is observing an object he classifies as dog. Now, a dog can be viewed from the front, the rear, the top, the bottom, right side, left side—any perspective—and he remains a dog. The philosophical assumption of this classification system is that the classes truly capture the real world. The name may change from language to language, but a dog is a dog is a dog.

With this outlook many sociologists observed the world. Instead of dogs, they saw communities.[8] They had no doubts. If they approached, say, Gervais from the north, west, east, or south, they all saw, and always saw, the same thing—the community Gervais. Later sociologists went to the same area. They asked slightly different questions of very different people. They didn't always see Gervais; they saw other things as well: Fairfield or Eldridge, for example. Many wanted to conclude that communities were disappearing, or that previous researchers were wrong.

Something obviously was wrong. But what was it? The error lay in assuming that logical classes correspond to the real world. One attempted way out is to make the observational technique correspond to the real world by fiat. We have seen that this does not solve the problem. The other way out is to observe the difference between analytical and taxonomic classes. The latter are real, and all members share equally in the defining characteristics. The former are relations such that if the relation changes the object observed also changes.

A person, X, may be classed as a friend by some people, as an enemy

11

by others. The biological individual does not change; indeed, he belongs in both categories. One sees him according to one's perspective. "Friend" is an analytical class. So is "community." It is probably true that the taxonomic classification is a special case of the analytic one.

Both naive operationalism which recreates the world in the image of its operations, and taxonomism which requires that the classifying operation correspond to the real world, lead to difficulties. This may really be the convergence that George Lundberg sees: neither admits error in classification. My position contradicts this.

I take it as a principle of scientific procedure that it is impossible to develop an error-free operational specification. If the logical classes were connected by variation in magnitude, this statement could read: I take it as a principle that there will always be error in measurement. This forces me to recognize that certain operations probably have less error than do others. I also allow for the possibility that a measure which has a minimal error at one point in time may have a sizable error at another.

The purpose of this volume is not to develop measuring or classifying techniques. The purpose is rather to develop a kind of argument consistent with the principle of errorful measurement. To anticipate my argument: this principle requires me to deny the possibility of asserting any relation with certainty; requires me to employ probability statistics; denies me the ability to decide whether probability is simply a matter of ignorance or a condition of the real world. This means that if probability is necessary to any part of my argument, it is necessary to all parts. But more of this later.

A FUNDAMENTAL CLASSIFICATION: THE DICHOTOMY

Consider the occurrence of an event which can have more than one outcome: age at first marriage is the event in question. Certainly, there is more than one outcome; the number of outcomes depends upon how fine a distinction in age one wishes to draw. Whatever the final number, certain differences must be defended. If "years" is employed, then "21 years" must be operationally distinct from "20 years" or "22 years"; or, in general, we may first require a difference between the interesting outcome and any other alternative. Thus, we must have at least a fundamental distinction between the interesting class (call it A) and any other alternative (call it "not A"—$\sim A$ for short). If this is all we know about our subject matter, then the contradiction of "not A" must be A.

INTRODUCTION

Some people, called semanticists, admit extra knowledge and insist that "if 22 years is 'not 21 years' then 23 years is 'not 22 years'; but the argument holds that negating $\sim A$ implies A, and we have shown this to be false." Stuff and nonsense. In the argument as developed, 23 years is not "not 22 years"; it is simply "not 21 years." The distinction between 22 and 23 years is forgotten; so, indeed, is the difference between 16 and 45 years. Each is equally "not 21 years."

It may turn out that a particular dichotomy is fruitless. But that is not the fault of logic. It is the fault of poor theory.

The reason that fruitless dichotomies flow from poor theory is this: theory contains our conceptual definitions. If these result in ambiguous or impossible operational specifications, they lead to bad results. Sometimes we employ dichotomies so commonplace they seem "natural" and take on the aura of taxonomic groups. For example, we borrow the male-female dichotomy from biology; this is natural. Yet we get into trouble soon enough, as a moment's reflection will reveal, when we try to apply this way of thinking to a masculinity-femininity "dichotomy." These latter are actually quantitative variables rather than dichotomous classes.

Not only must terms be defined, but, in order that propositions employing these terms can be tested, some operational specifications are needed. It may be that, conceptually, we are comfortable in the face of a quantitatively defined variable. This does not imply that, at the moment, we have any usable operational specification. Perhaps the only agreed-upon measure is a dichotomy. Simply because a quantity is our ideal does not mean that we should quit, pick up our marbles, and go home when the ideal cannot be met.

Moreover, it may well be that certain theoretical concepts are dichotomous in character, or that out of a set of alternatives only a specified pair are interesting. For various reasons, a dichotomy may represent the best of our operations. This being so, some rules for arriving at conclusions about dichotomy must be reached.

The argument has been inverted from the flow of history. The first kind of logic to be sufficiently formal for use in the social sciences was the kind that has been labeled Aristotelian. This is, essentially, a logic of dichotomous classes. It was something of an achievement to overthrow the rules of categorical logic. Nonetheless, the dichotomy is really the basic classification used. We shall see the significance of this assertion in our consideration of the rules of thought in the next chapter.

13

At the moment, we should recognize that an operational specification of a dichotomy can be exceedingly arbitrary. Consider a measure of the number of tractors per 1,000 acres of cropland harvested. We may dichotomize this by separating the units having 2.34 tractors or fewer from those having 2.35 or more. We may take our units, say counties, and divide them at the median—that number at which half the counties have fewer tractors and half have more. Clearly, a considerable amount of information is surrendered by such a dichotomy. Yet either of the foregoing examples could be a sensible specification of "mechanized farming" and "non-mechanized farming." Probably most researchers would prefer some theoretical defense rather than an appeal simply to making computation easier. But that is another story. The moral here is that contemporary research requires a knowledge of arguing from dichotomously classified data.

SCHEMATIC OUTLINE OF THE SUBSEQUENT ARGUMENT

Up to this point I have hoped only to provide a reader with some motivation for being concerned about the subject matter of this book. It may seem, now, that I have made rather unkind and pointed remarks about operationalism. This was my intent. I did so because I feel that the social scientists who most blindly support operationalism have tended to do so in opposition to theory. It may be true that some brands of theory have not been oriented to empirical research, and hence must be shown to be out of sympathy with the spirit of modern science. I do not propose to defend theory for its own sake. Indeed, the careful reader will note that I have a precise notion of theory rather than the vague argumentative kind that is happily received in some quarters. At the same time, I feel constrained to assert propositions which will enable research to generalize as well as to admit new problems. This seems most possible when science is oriented to theory rather than to any "operation." The latter orientation tends to put technique ahead of problems and can rapidly become sterile. The theory I envisage requires that much yet be done.

We must not let some "ideal" formulation of any field prevent us from activity today. We must work from where we are today—from the concepts we now employ, the arguments that are now permissible, the operations now available. That we need rules for argument is all but obvious; at some point, the scientist ceases his activity and reaches a conclusion. This conclusion must be shown to be correct. The scientist must cease his inquiry and engage in an argument. He must communicate his decisions ("findings") to others. He may or may not seek to *convince* them that he is right. But he must have a procedure that will insure the correctness of his inference. This is called logic. Accordingly, I will discuss elementary logic in the next chapter. This discussion proceeds from the belief that we need rules for drawing conclusions; the rules are called logic.

In the Western world, one kind of proposition which science has long sought to make has been called causal. Accordingly, we must assess the historical argument about causality and adopt a point of view. Clearly, this will lead us into problems of statistical inference. In particular, the issue of induction will require comment. This will be followed by a consideration of the status of chance in our thinking. Some comments upon the theoretical position given to ideas of probability are next in order. Formally, this will entail dealing with the probability syllogism and chisquare. The shortcut method will be shown to be consistent with the chi-square computation. In order to infer that some relation is an implication, one must first show that the relation is not that of independence. This obviously is related to the chi-square test of association. A mere denial of independence need not assure us that the relation was verified. Logical forms will be proposed as models for research design, much as mathematical models are currently employed. Various measures of the amount of association will be presented. These will include phi-square, Yule's Q, the coefficient of contingency, tetrachoric r, and others.

We will return to the problem of causality and assess some proposed measures. This will be followed by a demonstration of how the two-by-two table can be employed in the development of a scale. Other issues, such as joint effects, will be discussed and some techniques illustrated.

From this outline, it should be apparent that what follows is not a book for statisticians. It is a book directed at the bulk of social scientists. It begins with the assumption that the problem is the thing. It takes a simple statistical tool, the two-by-two table, and shows its relation to logic and to the intellectual history of problems of cause. I shall give a fairly thorough discussion of the statistics of the two-by-two table, keeping in mind the relation between traditional logic and statistical inference. I hope that such a treatment will free researchers from errors in logic, and theorists from the terrors of research.

CHAPTER 2

Categorical Logic

WE SAW in the first chapter that at a critical point a scientist engages in argument rather than inquiry. Whenever the scientist reaches a decision—that is, comes to a conclusion—he has to be able to demonstrate the correctness of this decision. The rules by which he defends his inference are called rules of logic. Or, more simply, logic is a system by which one reaches a conclusion.

We must not confuse being convinced about something with being able to demonstrate the thing we are convinced about. Conviction is probably an emotional state, while demonstration is an intellectual process. We are often convinced about things that are true (i.e., demonstrable), but we are not able to prove them. In many practical affairs, the distinction is so unnecessary as to seem foolish when raised with respect to a particular problem.

In science, on the other hand, the distinction is very important. Conviction is closely related to having reached a conclusion. Having reached a conclusion prevents inquiry. After all, a critical distinction between inquiry and argument is that in argument the answers are known while in inquiry they are unknown. Whenever the answers do become known or the individual is convinced that they are, inquiry ends and argument begins. But simple conviction does not imply proof. The scientist must make the distinction; and, further, he must have a system of logic which will enable him to justify his having reached his conclusion.

16

This book tries to present ways of thinking such that certain scientific decisions are justified. Often writers have accused statistics of simply proving the obvious. And this position has turned into an opposition to to the use of statistics as a way of thinking or reasoning in the social sciences.

Two important issues are clouded in that argument. First, we are usually convinced about the things we claim are obvious. But really, how obvious are ideas about the world—particularly ideas about the way people behave? Knowing that conviction and proof are different, we would expect to find that many things which were once obvious have been shown to be false. For example, it was once obvious that the biological fact of racial difference implied personality differences. While many people remain convinced of it, we know that the falsity of this obvious fact can be shown.

The second issue is the source of hypotheses to be tested. It happens that many of our most insightful hypotheses have come from what is often called "qualitative" research. If a scientist faces such an area of inquiry so new that it is impossible for him to deduce meaningful hypotheses from the current theory, how does he go about his business? If he asserts that he will use only a certain technique, he may be rejecting important data. Hence, it is not wise to predicate science simply on a technique.

What often happens is that the scientist proceeds by trial and error; as we shall see, at this stage sampling is often ignored. But who, at this stage, can really tell how one should sample? Moreover, in a relatively new area of inquiry, the scientist will be unable to state precisely what his problem is. This he may not know until he has more data than he has when he begins his activity. The fact is, he is likely to be trying to determine his problem, what constitutes his universe, what the correct hypotheses are. It is not surprising that the source of many hypotheses is qualitative research.

To those trained in scientific method that demands the rigorous test of precisely formulated hypotheses, it seems as if qualitative research fails to meet the requirements for good research. Those who test hypotheses often assert that qualitative research is sloppy. From the perspective of a refined logical system of research, this all seems to be true.

At the same time, we must remember that there is a difference between arriving at hypotheses and testing them. Both activities are essential to science. A curious thing happens at the point where this distinction is made. Those addicted to qualitative research assert that all that rigorous test does is to prove the obvious. Those who are addicted to quantitative research, on the other hand, belittle the others because of their lack of precision and refinement.

The fact of the matter is that with more knowledge, we can be more rigorous and refined in our testing of ideas, but this does not deny the importance of the activity that precedes the refinement. Both kinds of research are necessary: one as a source of ideas and hypotheses, the other as a test. It would be manifestly unscientific to willfully accept false hypotheses into our theory. And many of the obvious propositions are rejected after more rigorous test.

We said earlier that the basic scientific act includes the decision to accept or reject a given proposition. Following Felix Kaufmann,[1] we note that when a proposition is considered as a part of scientific theory, it either belongs or does not belong in science. That is, if a proposition is now a part of science, it either should remain there or it should be removed or at least modified. Similarly, if it is not yet a part of the theory, it should either be incorporated or it should remain outside.

If a proposition has been accepted into the theory, we say that it is verified. If it is rejected and is not replaced by another proposition, we say that it is invalidated. If one proposition is rejected and another has replaced it, we say that the former is falsified and the latter verified. Notice that in this framework, we falsify a proposition only if it is replaced by another which is verified. The falsification of propositions is relative to the acceptance of others. And science never really proves a proposition in an ultimate sense; it merely verifies the proposition.

This is related to the distinction between inquiry and research. Indeed, what we have previously called qualitative and quantitative research could easily be called respectively *inquiry*—the formulation of hypotheses, and *research*—the testing of them. The alert reader will have noted that at the first usage I put quotation marks around qualitative and quantitative. This was not accidental. I intended to suggest a question about the distinction.

We shall presently see that in science one uses both qualitative and quantitative logic. The decision to use one or the other ought not to be based on the personal preference of the scientist but should be a function of the kind of data used. If the assumptions of quantity are not met, the use of quantitative logic is not warranted. Moreover, quantitative logic itself is predicated upon the rules of qualitative logic. One of the greatest logical advances probably is the emergence of symbolic logic which enables one to incorporate mathematics into the same system of thinking as qualitative thinking.

It follows that the distinction between the two systems of thought is meaningless. I shall develop a system of thinking with a distinguishable set of postulates. A postulate is an assumption which is not tested but is accepted as true. As our data meet these postulates we will use the kind of thinking which those postulates permit. It is incorrect, then, to pose the question Which system of logic will I use? It is correct, however, to ask Which postulates of logic do my data satisfy? By abiding by the answer to the latter question, one will use whatever logic his data will permit. But he will use *only* whatever logic his data will permit. He will always be accountable for meeting the postulates fundamental to his argument. When his data are quantitative, he will use mathematics. But he will not use mathematics unless the postulates of quantity are satisfied. Statistics is not numerology—there is no mystic power in chi-square.

What follows is not intended as a full treatment of logic, nor is it designed to prepare the reader to become a logician. It will, however, be an introduction to logic and should provide the reader with a basis for correct thinking. Moreover, it will be formal. The reader should not expect to find an analysis of theoretical propositions.

The reader who has had some training in logic can regard this section as a refresher; at the same time, he might notice a difference between the symbolism used here and that used in his class in logic. I will not use symbolic logic except in a rudimentary way. Instead, I will follow the traditional system with certain fairly obvious exceptions.

Since science deals with propositions, the scientist ought to know something about propositions. A proposition is simply a statement which can be believed or doubted, which can be true or false. Ordinarily, I shall deal with what is called a two-term proposition, containing a subject and a predicate. Although grammatical form must be noted, the information contained in the proposition is more important.

A sentence of the order "All S is P" is not properly considered a proposition, since it asserts nothing about the real world. Until S and P are defined—given content—the sentence is simply a statement-form of a proposition. Logic deals, then, more with statement-forms than with propositions.

Before we proceed to analyze the forms of propositions, certain basic postulates must be accepted and understood. These are often called Aristotelian rules of thought. Our use of these ideas first propounded by Aristotle does not necessarily mean that we will use Aristotelian logic. The fact is, we won't. But it is also true that current non-Aristotelian logical systems still accept these rules of thought. Indeed, it is difficult to envisage a system that rejects them.

THE RULES OF THOUGHT

The law of identity. This asserts that a meaning is the same throughout an argument. If x is "boy," x means "boy" throughout the argument and never changes its meaning to, say, "girl." To have a term mean more than one thing is to introduce ambiguity into a discussion. Symbolically this rule would be written $S = S$. A modification sometimes found is $S = \sim(\sim S)$. This latter says that S is not not-S. The wave before a symbol makes that symbol negative: thus $\sim S$ means not-S.

The law of contradiction. This asserts that a thing (S) cannot be both another thing (P) and that other thing's contradiction ($\sim P$). An example: a boy cannot be both tall and short at the same time. Of course, one can say that the boy is tall from one point of view (his age) and short from another (all adult males); what this says, then, is that from the perspective of age, the boy cannot be both tall and short. The distinction is one of complexity and not the falsity of this law. Symbolically, this rule would be $S \neq (P \cdot \sim P)$. The equals sign cut by a slash signifies "is not" and the centered dot signifies "and."

The law of the excluded middle. This asserts that a thing (S) must be either P or not P. That is, in speaking of height, the boy must be either tall or not tall. Included in the latter term (not tall) could be "average" as well as "short." When these terms are used as predicates of the subject, the subject must be one of them. When one term is singled out to be symbolized as P, any other variation of the predicate would be not P. Symbolically, this would be $S = (P V \sim P)$; in this parenthetic term, the V means "or."

20

CATEGORICAL LOGIC

FORMS OF PROPOSITIONS

There are, classically, four forms of the two-term proposition. These represent all possible combinations of two dichotomized variables. One is the mode of the proposition, whether affirmative or negative; the other is the quantity of the proposition, whether all the members of a class or only some of them are referred to. We will denote them by the letters traditionally assigned to them.

A. *The universal affirmative.* Traditionally, this has the form "All S is P." Since the class S implies another class $\sim S$, and since a similar condition holds for P, it is apparent that the two-term proposition is useful in providing us with specific information. In this case, we can see that the universal affirmative proposition "All S is P" provides us with the information that the joint, or copulated, class $(S \cdot \sim P)$ is null, i.e., has no members. This can be visualized in a two-by-two table.

	P	$\sim P$
S		0
$\sim S$		

Further, the proposition does not give us the information that there are any S; it merely asserts that if there were, none would be $\sim P$.

E. *The universal negative.* This takes the form of "No S is P." This proposition clearly asserts the null character of the copulated class $S \cdot P$. In tabular form, this proposition would be

	P	$\sim P$
S	0	
$\sim S$		

I. *The particular affirmative.* The form of this proposition is "Some S is P." This provides us with the information that the copulated class $S \cdot P$ is not null. While it negates the E form, it does not necessarily negate the A form. That is, if it is true that all S is P, it is also true that some are. In tabular form, this would be

	P	$\sim P$
S	x	
$\sim S$		

21

where x indicates that, given the existence of S, an indeterminate part will be located in the indicated cell.

O. *The particular negative.* This has the form "Some S is not P"; the information provided is that the copulated class $S \cdot \sim P$ is not null. Either the E form or the I form could be true and the O form could also be true. In tabular form

	P	~P
S		x
~S		

The reader must notice that the proposition "Some S is P" is not the same as "Only some S is P." The two propositions provide us with different information. What the difference is, the reader can determine for himself.

RELATIONS BETWEEN PROPOSITIONS

Two propositions, Q and R, are related in the kind of knowledge one has of the second proposition, R, when the first proposition, Q, is affirmed or denied. It is clear that Q can be either true or false; similarly, R can be true or false. We can, then, visualize possible relations between propositions by the use of a two-by-two table similar to the one we used in discussing statement-forms; the difference here is that we are dealing with propositions rather than terms of a proposition. Thus our table would be

	Q	~Q
R		
~R		

Initially, we can see that we can work out a system of combining the truth or falsity of these propositions. Thus,

> Q and R can be true together;
> Q can be true and R false;
> Q can be false and R true;
> Q and R can be false together.

Whenever one of these joint conditions is false, or not possible, we can

22

symbolize it by entering a 0 in the proper cell of our table. Thus, if Q and R cannot both be true, our table would appear

	Q	$\sim Q$
R	0	
$\sim R$		

Similarly, if the joint condition that Q is true and R is false is itself false, our table would be

	Q	$\sim Q$
R		
$\sim R$	0	

If the joint condition that Q is false and R is true is false, our table would be

	Q	$\sim Q$
R		0
$\sim R$		

If the joint condition that both Q and R are false is false, the table would be

	Q	$\sim Q$
R		
$\sim R$		0

The reader will observe that it seems possible to enter in the table combinations of zeros other than those given. This we shall do; we shall find that some of these possible entries are not particularly useful in analyzing relations between propositions. Others, however, are possible and will find important usage in our system of thinking.

Some of these double entries will have zeros in the same row or column, e.g.

	Q	$\sim Q$
R	0	0
$\sim R$		

This asserts that the proposition R is never true; hence we need not consider its relation to the proposition Q.

Two double entries are of interest to us, however; these are the possible entries in the diagonal cells:

	Q	~Q
R	0	
~R		0

	Q	~Q
R		0
~R	0	

The information in the first of these two tables is that Q and R are neither true together nor false together. When one is true, the other is false. The information in the second table is that Q and R are either true together or false together. One is never true and the other false.

Finally, we should note the situation where all combinations are possible. That is, none of the four cells in the table is null, and all can possibly exist:

	Q	~Q
R		
~R		

Propositions with this relationship can be true together, false together, or one true and the other false. Thus, given knowledge of Q, whether its affirmation or denial, one has no knowledge of R. Such statements are said to be *independent* of each other.

Another special relation between propositions is *equivalence*. Two propositions are said to be equivalent when each conveys the same information as the other. Thus "All S is P" and "The copulated class S · ~P is null" are equivalent because they convey precisely the same information.

With this background, I shall proceed to discuss certain specific types of relations. Each is built upon what has been given in the section above.

For convenience, I shall use the statement-forms given earlier in my analysis of relations between propositions.

Implication and subimplication. If when one statement is true another is also true, though the second statement may be true or false when the first is false, we say that the first statement implies the second. Let "All S is P" be Q, and "Some S is P" be R. If Q (is true), then R (is true). That is, if "All S is P" is true, it immediately follows that "Some S is P" is also true. This relationship can be visualized in the following table:

	Q	~Q
R		
~R	0	

From this we can see that "If Q, then R" is a relation such that the joint truth of Q and falsity of R is denied. We should remember that we are dealing only with the formal requirements for logical relations. Remembering an earlier distinction between statement-forms and propositions, we must observe that one proposition does not imply another unless there are uniform substitutions of corresponding instances in the statement-forms involved in the inference.

If when one statement is true another may be true or false, though when the first is false the second is also false, we say that the relation of subimplication exists between the two statements. This may be visualized in our table as

	Q	~Q
R		0
~R		

For example, let "Some S is P" be Q, and "All S is P" be R. If Q, then we can say nothing about R (hereafter we shall use the question mark to symbolize the lack of a necessary truth value in an argument), but if ~Q, then ~R. Analyzing the content of Q and R, we can see that if "Some S is P" is true, it may or may not be true that "All S is P." However, if "Some S is P" is false, "All S is P" is also false, for "Some S is P" can be false if and only if "No S is P" is true.

Looking at the table for implication and that for subimplication, the reader will realize that in combining the conditions asserted in each into one table we get a table whose diagonals are both zero. That is, we can consider a relationship which is such that both propositions can be true together or false together.

	Q	$\sim Q$
R		0
$\sim$R	0	

This is of the form "If and only if Q, then R." While we may desire propositions of this form in our science, we must not confuse it with the implicatory form, "If Q, then R."

The contrary relations. If when one proposition is true another is false, but when the first is false the second may or may not be true, we say that the one is the contrary of the other. In our table, with Q as our first proposition, and R the second,

	Q	$\sim Q$
R	0	
$\sim$R		

Let "All S is P" be Q, and "No S is P" be R. If Q, then $\sim$R, but if $\sim Q$, then ? The inability to infer anything about R if Q is false can be seen, in this case, by observing that if "No S is P" is false, it may or may not be true that "All S is P." If "Some S is P" is true, "No S is P" is false, but "Some S is P" is not the same as "All S is P."

If when one proposition is false another is true, but when the first is true the other may or may not be true, we say the relation is that of sub-contrariety. In our table,

	Q	$\sim Q$
R		
$\sim$R		0

Let "Some S is P" be Q, and "Some S is not $\sim P$" be R. If Q is false, then R is true; while if Q is true, R may or may not be: if "All S is P" happens to be true, then Q is true and R is false. The student should remember that the statement-form "Some S is P" is not the equivalent of "Only some S is P."

Again, a glance at these two tables reveals that they can be so combined that the diagonal cells both have zero entries:

	Q	$\sim Q$
R	0	
$\sim R$		0

This table describes the relation existing between two propositions which are neither true together nor false together. If the truth of one proposition implies the falsity of the other, and the falsity of the first implies the truth of the second, the two are said to contradict each other. The student should reflect on the difference between contradiction and simple contrariety. The two are not the same, though both have one condition in common: that is, the truth of Q implies the falsity of R. At that point their similarity ends. Any theory which utilizes contrary relations as though they were contradictory ones contains fallacious reasoning.

An example of contradiction can be seen if we let "All S is P" be Q and "Some S is not P" be R. If Q is true, R cannot be, and if Q is false, R must be true. Further, if R is true, Q must be false; and if R is false, Q must be true.

We shall now turn our attention to using these relations in drawing inferences.

WAYS OF REACHING CONCLUSIONS

The syllogism. Knowing something about the forms of propositions and the relations that exist between these forms, we must now put them together in such a way that they may be used. We have already noted that formal logic considers only the form, and not the content, of the proposition in question. Thus, we should be aware that there are at least two orders of fallacies possible in our thinking. There are formal fallacies, or incorrect reasoning; and material fallacies, or errors in the content of the proposition.

We can illustrate the difference by using a fairly well-known syllogism. In this case we shall reach a logically correct conclusion which is known to be false. By definition, a syllogism is a two-premised argument containing an inference. That is, the syllogism contains two premises and a conclusion. The logical question is whether or not the premises supplied us with the information which requires the conclusion as stated. Thus we might argue:

> All mice are bigger than fleas.
> All fleas are bigger than cats.
> All mice are bigger than cats.

The first two propositions are called the premises, the first being the major premise and the second the minor. The third proposition is the conclusion. The logical question is Does the conclusion follow from the premise?

Each of these propositions is a two-term proposition; and, in this case, of the A form (see p. 21). Looking at the conclusion, we will designate "mice" as the subject and denote it by S; "bigger than cats" is the predicate term which we will denote as P. Observation reveals that these classes of objects appear in the premises. In the first we find the term "mice," and in the second premise we find the term "bigger than cats." Now, it happens that the term "fleas" occurs in both of the premises. This we call the middle term, and we will label it M.

The reader should not assume that all syllogisms are of this order; that is, the subject of the conclusion is not always the subject of the major premise. Nor, for that matter, need the propositions be of the A form. However, every (good) syllogism always has these three terms: the subject of the conclusion, the predicate of the conclusion, and a middle term. He should notice that, in this case, if the subject of the minor premise had been, say, "horses," there would be no connection between the two propositions. They would then have been independent, and, clearly, no conclusion could have been drawn.

The reader may reflect here upon the importance of the law of identity. If we had not accepted that as a postulate, we would be stymied at this point. That law, it will be remembered, said that $S = S$—in this case $M = M$. If we did not have a rule of this sort, M could be its contradiction ($\sim M$) which would give us four terms, plus complete independence between the two premises. (In general, the reader should continually integrate previous statements with this discussion of reasoning.)

Getting back to the illustration of the syllogism, let us proceed to analyze the premises to see if we must reach the same conclusion as was asserted. By labeling our terms S, M, and P, we see that the first proposition gives us the information that the copulated class $S \cdot \sim M$ is null.

The second premise gives us the information that the copulated class $M \cdot \sim P$ is null. The conclusion asserts that the copulated class $S \cdot \sim P$ is null. The question is If the first two statements are true, is the third one also true?

To determine whether or not that is the case, we will construct a complex table and enter the information given us in the premises. Then we will see whether or not that agrees with the information asserted in the conclusion. Our table is built on the dichotomies M and $\sim M$; P and $\sim P$; and S and $\sim S$. Under t, we enter the total information supplied by the premises. Thus the first, $S \cdot \sim M = 0$, is entered in the column labeled t under $\sim M$ and to the extreme right of S. The second, $M \cdot \sim P = 0$, is entered in row t under M and directly under $\sim P$.

	M			~M		
	P	~P	t	P	~P	t
S		0		0		0 0
~S		0				
t		0				

Now, since the first entry was 0, it follows that the cells to the left of this figure must also be 0. Since the second entry was 0, it follows that the cells above it also are 0. That is, there are no negative frequencies—something cannot sensibly occur a minus number of times. Whatever figures are entered must add up to zero, and the only two numbers whose sum is zero when one of them is not a negative number is $0 + 0$.

The conclusion had asserted that $S \cdot \sim P = 0$. Do we have the information from our premises such that this conclusion is forced on us? Looking at our table, we see that, under M, the copulated class $S \cdot \sim P$ is zero; but this accounts for only part of the total class $S \cdot \sim P$. We must look to that copulated class $S \cdot \sim P$ under $\sim M$. We find that that is also zero. Hence, we must agree that the assertion $S \cdot \sim P = 0$ is true. This means that the statement "All S is P" follows from the premises. And this means that the proposition "All mice are bigger than cats" follows from the premises.

Formally, the argument is correct, or valid, as some logicians prefer. But, empirically, we know that it is incorrect. Not all mice (if any) are bigger than cats. The error is a material one. Thus, while one may know how to reason correctly, one must always be certain of the correctness of his premise. However, the student should note that the proposition "All mice are bigger than fleas" is itself a conclusion, as was the second premise, "All fleas are bigger than cats."

The empirical question is, how does one get content into form? I cannot give a complete answer, but it must be observed that much scientific activity is involved in asserting the correctness of the premises from which conclusions are reached. We must follow rules of logic which permit us to reach the conclusion that our premise is a correct one. The formal character of the logic is no different from any other form of inference. We must look for more than logical rigor in our argument; science does not deal with a make-believe world. The problem of content can never be avoided.

Let us now modify the form of the syllogism so that one of the premises is of a particular form. Suppose that the major premise had been "Some mice are bigger than fleas." Using the same symbols, this gives us the information that the copulated class $S \cdot M$ is not null; that is, given some mice, at least some of them are bigger than fleas. The minor premise gives us the information it did before, i.e., $M \cdot \sim P = 0$. Let us enter this in the table and see what conclusion is possible.

This time, we will have to enter an x in the column headed t under M. We still enter 0 in row t under $\sim P$ in the M part of the table:

	M				$\sim M$		
	P	$\sim P$	t		P	$\sim P$	t
S	x		0	x			
$\sim S$			0				
t			0				

Now, since we enter a zero, we know the cells above it must also contain zeros. This means that x under t comes from the cell $S \cdot P \cdot M$; $x + 0 = x$. What can we conclude from this information?

The previous conclusion, $S \cdot \sim P = 0$, does not necessarily follow, since we have no information about the classes $S \cdot P \cdot \sim M$ and $S \cdot \sim P \cdot \sim M$. However, we do know that some S is P. Thus, we find that, given a particular premise, we cannot conclude a universal proposition. At best, we can conclude only a particular proposition. Again, the reader should note we are dealing only with the formal, not the material, element in reasoning.

For our third example, let us consider the syllogism both of whose premises are of a particular form. That is, let us consider the argument

> Some mice are bigger than fleas.
> Some fleas are bigger than cats.
> Some mice are bigger than cats.

Is this conclusion warranted?

Using the same symbolism, we find that the first premise gives the information that the copulated class $S \cdot M$ is not null. The second gives the information that the copulated class $M \cdot P$ is not null. The conclusion asserts that the copulated class $S \cdot P$ is not null. The question is, does this necessarily follow?

In our table, we enter an x in column t across from S under M. Similarly, we enter an x in row t under P in section M:

	M				~M		
	P	~P	t		P	~P	t
S			x				
~S							
t	x						

We cannot go further and enter values in the cells, since we do not know how the x values are distributed. It follows that we can come to no conclusion. This is a significant finding. (If we have particular premises, we can come to no conclusion in traditional logic.)

The reader should ask himself how many propositions in the social sciences are universal, and how many are particular. We can assert, for example, that some delinquents come from broken homes, and that some broken homes result from cross-cultural marriages. What can we infer about the relationship of delinquency to cross-cultural marriages? Through the use of categorical logic, nothing can be inferred.

Yet this form of proposition typifies most of the empirical propositions of sociology. We seem to have reached an impasse. We know that the scientist must, at some point, engage in argument to demonstrate his conclusions. The validity of any argument depends, in part, upon the form of the propositions. (Most of our propositions are particular ones.

But one can reach no necessary conclusion, using the syllogism, from particular propositions. There is a limit, apparently, to the utility of categorical logic.)

We will have to determine a set of postulates and logical rules to permit inferences from particular propositions, or else admit we can come to no rigorous conclusions. This latter choice commits us to an absence of scientific rigor. Our choice, then, is to seek a logic which deals with less than universal propositions. This, indeed, makes up the major part of any book on statistics. For this other logic deals with probability statements, the basis of statistical reasoning.

Before discussing probability as a logical system, we should note certain other types of reasoning. In each case, however, we will again observe the limitations of categorical logic to deal with the empirical propositions of sociology.

The alternative syllogism. The alternative syllogism is a two-premised argument which contains, in its major premise, a statement of alternatives. Depending upon whether it is a weak or a strong alternative, the minor premise contains an affirmation or a denial of one of the alternatives. A third proposition, the consequent, follows from the two premises. Letting P stand for one proposition, and Q the other, the major premise, asserting "Either P or Q" is symbolized as $P \vee Q$.

In the case of the weak alternative, the propositions on the major premise may both be true, but they cannot both be false. We can say, then, that the symbolic form $P \vee Q$ of the weak alternative is the equivalent of the form $\sim(\sim P \cdot \sim Q)$. This would be represented as

$$P \qquad \sim P$$

$$Q$$

$$\sim Q \qquad\qquad 0$$

Looking at our table, we can see that the affirmation of P gives us no information about the truth or falsity of Q; similarly, the affirmation of Q gives us no information about the truth or falsity of P. However, the denial of either P or Q implies the truth of the other.

For example, let our major premise be "Either some S is P or some S is not P." To affirm "Some S is P" does not tell us whether the statement "Some S is not P" is true. Both can be true. But the only condition for arriving at a conclusion is to deny one of the antecedents. "Some S

is P" can be denied only if "No S is P" is true. If "No S is P" is true, it follows that "Some S is not P" is also true.

The correct system of inference, from the weak alternative, is to assert PVQ in the major premise; deny either P or Q in the minor premise, and conclude the other alternative. It happens that, in scientific inquiry, we may have a set of hypotheses which we think solves a particular problem. This set may be composed of two or more alternative propositions. If they constitute a weak alternative system—i.e., if all may be true—the logical system involves the successive denial of hypotheses until only one remains. Clearly, this form of reasoning is limited; it necessitates, for formal proof, a complete set of alternatives in order to infer the one which is not denied.

The strong alternative, sometimes called the disjunctive syllogism, involves the case where the propositions contained in the major premise might both be false, but cannot both be true. Symbolically, the form PVQ of the strong alternative is the equivalent of the form $\sim (P \cdot Q)$. This would be represented as

$$P \qquad \sim P$$

$$Q \qquad 0$$

$$\sim Q$$

We can see that the denial of either P or Q implies nothing about the other alternative. But the affirmation of P implies the falsity of $\sim Q$, and the affirmation of Q implies the falsity of P.

An example, in terms of statement-forms, would be "Either all S is P or no S is P." Both of these may be false if the true state of affairs is that the statements "Some S is P" and "Some S is not P" are both true. Hence the denial of either alternative does not, in this case, imply the truth of the other. However, to affirm one does imply the falsification of the other.

The reader can easily see that a complete disjunctive would be one where P and Q are neither true together nor false together. In our table this would be

$$P \qquad \sim P$$

$$Q \qquad 0$$

$$\sim Q \qquad \qquad 0$$

In such a case, one can reach a conclusion either by affirming or denying one alternative in the minor premise. This, the reader will observe, obtains only if the major premise asserts a contradiction. Moreover, he will observe that the major premise of the weak alternative asserts a subcontrariety while the major premise of the strong alternative asserts a contrariety.

The hypothetical syllogism. The statement-form of the hypothesis is that of the implicatory relation; the student will recognize the form of the hypothesis as "If P, then Q." The hypothetical syllogism asserts, in the major premise, this relationship between the propositions P and Q. The problem is to determine the nature of the minor premise such that a necessary conclusion follows:

Remembering the necessity for uniform substitutions of corresponding instances of the statement-forms making up the propositions P and Q, we note that the assertion "If P, then Q" is the equivalent of saying that the truth of P and the falsity of Q cannot jointly occur.

$$P \qquad \sim P$$

$$Q$$

$$\sim Q \quad 0$$

From this we see that "If P, then Q" is such that

> When P is true, Q is also true;
> when P is false, Q may or may not be true;
> when Q is true, P may or may not be true;
> when Q is false, P is also false.

This information provides us with the kind of minor premise necessary to draw an inference. We can come to necessary conclusions if the minor premise (1) affirms the truth of P (2) denies the truth of Q. The denial of P cannot lead to any knowledge about Q; and the affirmation of Q contains no knowledge as to the truth of P.

In Chapter 1, we saw that much scientific activity includes the creation of hypotheses. Another kind of scientific activity, we said, includes the *testing* of hypotheses. We further asserted that a proposition being tested is a hypothesis, and that if the proposition is not being tested it is not a hypothesis. Now, we can see that most of the activity of *research* involves the test of implicatory propositions.

Accordingly, we will let proposition P refer to antecedent, and proposition Q refer to consequent. Testing hypotheses, then, means testing asserted relations between antecedents and consequents. I need scarcely comment that, to be a hypothesis, the proposition must be testable.

It is clear that the denial of the consequent implies a denial of the antecedent. Many, however, may overlook the fact that the presence of the consequent does not allow the inference of the antecedent, though at the same time the antecedent is not denied. The logic of falsifying hypotheses is much more rigorous than that of proving them.

We noted earlier that much scientific activity really amounts to choosing among alternative propositions. In the weak alternative, the minor premise had to be a denial of one of the alternatives. Since the test of a hypothesis most rigorously demonstrates the falsity of asserted antecedents, it follows that science proceeds on the use of both the alternative and the hypothetical syllogisms. Quite often, the hypotheses of science are not demonstrated; but, since all others are falsified and since the hypotheses are not denied, those of science are accepted as accounting for the data.

One more point must be noted. The condition for testing hypotheses is that at least one cell in our table must be null. Suppose, for example, that we assert a relation between P and Q, and test it in a set of experiments. Suppose, further, that as a result we fail to get the null cell in $P \cdot \sim Q$, although the proportion may approach nullity. Logically, we fail to have a universal proposition upon which the whole structure can rest. What conclusions can we reach? By means of categorical logic, nothing. The reader may apprehend that, in this case, one might be able to argue in terms of probability statements. If that is so, it is even more necessary for us to develop a logical system which will include inferences based upon probability statements.

CHAPTER 3

Problems in the Proof of Causality

ONE of Western man's common ideas about the world is causality. Most such common ideas are vague and fuzzy; most are probably wrong, but one persists: that a cause is somehow necessary to an event. How a cause works, and what it is about a cause that makes it a cause, are seldom discussed. It may be just as well.

In the search for causes, two basic formulations of the problem have been developed. One may be called causal pluralism. Essentially, this says that the world is made up of a set of causal systems which are independent of each other. Thus, a baseball game at a specified field is part of a causal system; my behavior at home is part of another. It may be that I listen to the game on the radio or see it on television. In either event, although the game may determine my behavior (especially if I am rooting for one of the teams), my behavior will have no influence upon the game. My cheers are to no avail; I am a helpless mass, to all intents and purposes a bucket of cells—no more.

This formulation is at least a pragmatically happy one. It lets one pursue causes in one area without being concerned about causes in others. One can study the internal combustion engine without studying the engineer. Biology can be studied apart from chemistry, astronomy apart from both. A real division of labor is possible.

Causal pluralism must not be confused with multiple causation theories, which are of two kinds. One says that, as in the case of death, many causes can produce the same consequent; heart attack, cancer, gunshot wounds, and so on are all causes of a similar consequent: death. The second kind of multiple causation is more complex. Without affirming or denying the former idea, the latter holds that a consequent results from the coexistence of two or more factors; if one of these factors exists without the others, the consequent does not occur. Consider the argument that poverty does not itself cause delinquency; but poverty *in conjunction with* a strong desire to get the material symbols of success will cause delinquency or crime. These ideas are just complex formulations of the idea of cause, and introduce nothing really new. Causal pluralism would hold that causes of death are a system of forces which exist (probably) independently of causes of delinquency. Some caution in using this example must be noted: how do we classify murder? Despite such ugly problems, causal pluralism allowed people to be in the cause-finding business without raising the question of finding all causes.

Pragmatic solutions do not necessarily correspond to a real world. The fact that one cannot tell the difference between a lie and a truth does not make the former true and the latter false. One may act as if a lie were true, but this does not really change anything. That is, there are those who deny causal pluralism. Some philosophers argue for what is known as causal monism.

Causal monism holds that the universe is composed of a single causal system. Not only are delinquency and cause of death part of a more general scheme, but everything else is too. Consider the question contained in the following. There is a cause for the number of fish in the sea; there is a cause for John's hair's being red; are these connected? The pluralist would answer "No" (if cautious, "Probably no"); the monist would say "Yes."

If one includes poets, theologians, philosophers, and other thinkers, probably a monistic theory would turn out to be the kind most frequently espoused. This is the result, I surmise, of our intellectual history. If everything has a cause, and if today's events were essentially or figuratively caused yesterday, then this causal analysis can be carried back to an original creation or first cause. Whenever one attempts to discover what caused the cause, he tends to go back to a first cause.

It is one thing to believe in first causes; it is another to prove them. Many propositions have been offered; none, to my knowledge, is testable. At least, since they begin with the present and go back to the first cause, the present is consistent with the proposed first cause. And since we cannot falsify the present (it *does* exist), we cannot under any circumstances falsify the antecedents. Since we can never describe the conditions under which the asserted first cause will be falsified, it cannot be tested.

Since propositions about first causes cannot be tested, they are not encompassed by the mood of modern science. The resolution of this has been simple: refuse to ask the question. If the question is not raised, no position need be taken. It is not that the modern scientist has proved there is no first cause; he simply finds such an idea is a bit embarrassing, and ignores it. Modern science does not rest upon any particular proposition of first cause, and can exist independent of any such argument. But this does not mean that no proposition about first causes can be right; it simply means that none can be verified. They can, however, be believed, and many are.

This discussion does not assert what cause is. Some idea of necessity seems to be required. The imagery conjured up by reference to cause is probably varied. A common one must be something like the meshing of gears. Indeed, this mechanistic notion of cause was apparently involved in the invention of the calculus. The idea is simple: adding a very tiny increment to x *caused* the increment to y.

In assessing the history of man's argument for causes, it should always be borne in mind that man looked for causes. He observed an event; he looked for the cause. He saw a rock drop to the ground—or felt an apple hit him on the head. A man is walking on a city street; a cigaret drops on his hat. So he looks for a cause. Man searched for the truth; and one of the truths he sought was causes of events.

The argument of David Hume. In addition to the idea that every event has a cause, it was accepted that each similar cause has a similar effect, and like effects have like causes. This was regarded as a law of nature. A question that had to be answered was How do you know such a law to be true?

By the time David Hume addressed himself to the problem, a school of psychology had begun to emerge. The idea had developed that the mind was a "blank slate" that received sense impressions and connected them in various ways. The connections between these impressions were not the same as the impressions themselves. One was in this way connected to the world through his senses (a good connection existed if the

senses were good). To Hume, there were three sorts of connections sufficient to explain all relations of ideas. These were resemblance, contiguity, and cause and effect.

That these principles serve to connect ideas will not, I believe, be much
doubted. A picture naturally leads our thoughts to the original (resemblance): the mention of one apartment in a building naturally introduces an enquiry or discourse concerning the others (contiguity); and
if we think of a wound, we can scarcely forbear reflecting on the pain
which follows it (cause and effect).[1]

He goes on to say that these three principles are sufficient; for example,
contrast may be considered as a kind of mixture of causation and resemblance. "Where two objects are contrary, the one destroys the other;
that is, the cause of its annihilation, and the idea of the annihilation of
an object, implies the idea of its former existence."[2]

Just as we have referred in the first two chapters to form and content,
Hume distinguishes between relations of ideas (purely formal) and matters of fact. He does not extensively treat the formal character of the
latter. His interest lies elsewhere: relations of ideas like those of geom-
etry do not depend upon this world, whereas matters of fact are connected to this world. The evidence of their truth is not like that of the
mathematical proposition: something assumed to be true in mathematics
cannot, in that argument, be doubted. But every statement of fact has a
reasonable contrary which is possible. Thus,

That the sun will not rise tomorrow is no less intelligible a proposition,
and implies no more contradiction than the affirmation, that it will rise.
We should in vain, therefore, attempt to demonstrate its falsehood.[3]

He argues that whereas all reasonings about matters of fact are founded
on the relation of cause and effect, no knowledge of cause is possible.
He categorically rejects chance, and subscribes to an "ignorance" theory
of probability. Then he argues that if you observe a fact and ask for the
reason for that fact, you will be given another fact, and eventually you
must terminate with some fact which is present in your memory. Or,
giving us a rather unhappy alternative, you must allow that your belief
is entirely without foundation.

How does the human mind make these connections, which are necessary bridges between the past and the future? It is all a matter of custom;
custom is the "great guide of human life."

It is that principle alone which renders our experience useful to us, and makes us expect, for the future, a similar train of events with those which have appeared in the past. Without the influence of custom, we should be entirely ignorant of every matter of fact beyond what is immediately present to the memory and senses.[4]

But what of the necessary connection between causes and effects? Is this really merely custom, mere habitual connections in our minds? Doesn't cause influence things out there? Well, yes; but we can never know it; and knowing cause is the crux. As a matter of fact,

When we look about us towards external objects, and consider the operation of causes, we are never able, in a single instance, to discover any power or necessary connexion; any quality, which binds the effect to the cause, and renders the one an infallible consequence of the other. We only find, that the one does actually, in fact, follow the other. The impulse of one billiard-ball is attended with motion in the second. This is the whole that appears to the *outward* senses. The mind feels no sentiment or *inward* impression from this succession of objects: Consequently there is not, in any single, particular instance of cause and effect, any thing which can suggest the idea of power or necessary connexion.[5]

All that is there are impressions, connected by habit. When we observe a uniform set of instances of one event's being followed by another, we feel a new sentiment or impression—the customary connection in thought and imagination of this sequence. Thus, we can never prove cause; we can only apprehend a customary mental operation.

Hume is not without his critics as well as his followers. Some criticisms were undoubtedly mere denials, just as many affirmations were simple echoes. It has become old-hat to point out that Hume, in his sensationalist psychology which supports his doctrine of impressions, appeals to a causal argument. But Hume never really rejected causality; he merely rejected knowledge of it.

A more fundamental criticism, I think, rests upon two points. First, Hume never understood nor made problematic the idea of custom. As a matter of fact, custom as he used it is a question-begging concept. It is, fundamentally, a summary of certain observations—one makes this connection, again, again, again, and again: ergo, he has the custom of making this connection. How do you explain this connection? Why, the man has a custom of making this connection. This circularity (made a bit bald in this paragraph) is hardly a convincing argument.

My second criticism is of the notion of impression as the necessary result of sensation. Unfortunately, Hume did not know our contemporary social psychology, especially the symbolic interactionist school. Hume took images to be a matter of the relation of a unique individual to the world about him. How the interaction of one man with another is necessary for a symbol to have meaning is foreign to Hume. Had he been aware of this, his appeal to custom could have taken a different form.

I should also point out that Hume merely rejected our being able to make assertions demonstrating causal connections. He, like the others, looked at the world to find causes. His conception of the world required him to seek sense impressions of causes. This he was unable to do—understandably.

A traditional way out: look for associations. One technique of many scientists when faced with a difficult task is to change the job. Instead of looking for causes, you look for something else. Thus, you may find a fact following a fact. Never make the mistake of calling the first fact a cause of the second. Simply assert that the two facts are associated with each other.

This may seem an exaggerated formulation. It is almost a direct quotation from Karl Pearson. The actual quotation follows:

As a method of predicting the experience *likely* in the future from the experience of the past, the summary of the past expressed by function or under the category of causation has done immense service. But it is incomplete in itself, for it gives no measure of the variation in experience, and it has trammelled the human mind, because it has led to a conceptual limit dominating actual experience. We have tried to subsume all things under a perfectly inelastic category of cause and effect. It has led to our disregarding the fundamental truth that nothing in the universe repeats itself; we cannot classify by sameness, but only by likeness. Resemblance connotes variation and variation marks limited not absolute contingency. How often, when a new phenomenon has been observed, do we hear the question asked: What is the cause of it? A question which it may be absolutely impossible to answer, whereas the question: To what degree are other phenomena associated with it? may admit of easy solution, and result in invaluable knowledge.[6]

Because of the similarity of this to Hume's argument, one may expect to find Pearson holding a similar assumption about the role of the scientist. Pearson develops his argument by considering perception, and how "breaks" or "gaps" in observations create a need for probability statements. Interestingly, for Pearson man (the scientist) is passive toward the world, as he was for Hume. Sense impressions impinge upon him, creating perceptions. But perceptions never allow for the observation of sameness, only of likeness.

Other dodges than an appeal to probability as signifying ignorance have been offered. One of the uses for the ideal type is precisely of this order. The late Howard Becker claimed that "of course" nothing in the world ever truly recurs, but "for the purposes at hand" we act as if it did.[7] In so doing, we create a type which is not really a representation of a unique world of fact. Thus a cell in biology is an ideal type; so is a group.

My criticism of Pearson does not use this particular way out of the difference between sameness and likeness. Pearson was a statistician. Many of the early empiricists went into the field guarded by such wonderful devices as the Pearsonian r or chi-square (this latter I shall presently employ). Pearson, after all, contributed much to the field of statistical theory. As a matter of fact, it is his ideas of correlation and variation which are most directly opposed to the earlier doctrines of cause.

Here Pearson almost hit the bullseye. But, like Hume, he accepted the historical version of the problem—how to find causes—and deciding that none could be proved, gave up the venture. He saw, for example, that one could correlate various measures without being able to assert that one caused the other. An example (not his) is the correlation between the increased use of cigarets by American males and the increased incidence of breast cancer in American females during the same period. One would hardly argue that a causal connection exists, no matter how "customary the perceptual connection." From examples of this kind he concluded that correlation, no matter how close to unity, does not warrant an inference of cause. But a statistician could hardly be expected to go back upon the contention of statistical inference. Some relation other than chance is shown to exist. If not cause, what is it? The answer: association.

A generation of researchers has demonstrated its sophistication by proudly denying causality when interpreting linear correlations. Does cigaret-smoking cause lung cancer? Well, the more one smokes, the more likely one is to have lung cancer (the more one perceives an object smoking, the more likely one is to perceive the same object having lung cancer). But no causal connection is shown—only association. Now, this may be true. An alternative accounting of a linear relation between amount of smoking and incidence of lung cancer is easily available. Sup-

42

pose that, in cases of addiction to smoking, the same things that cause cancer also cause increased desire to smoke. Were this so, the same correlation would be manifest in the data.

A close reading of the preceding paragraph will suggest something that Pearson, and those who have shared his viewpoint, missed. Although statistical inference may warrant only assertions of association, there are various kinds of association. Consider the relation between color of eyes and natural color of hair. Clearly, these are associated, and it does not require much sophistication in genetics to explain the association. But, what about, say, the speed with which a rock is thrown and the likelihood that a window will break when hit with the thrown rock? High speed is likely to be associated with high probability of breakage. No one would say that this kind of association is exactly like the former.

This, I think, is the issue: We generally have more information than that contained in the statistically formal argument. Although the formal statistical argument may lend itself to an inference of association, the admission of other knowledge will often permit the modification of the idea association. If, for example, it is known that a change in A is associated with a change in B we know something more than if we had merely correlated measurements of A with measurements of B.

The clue is quite simple: Pearson, like Hume—like everyone else—looked for causes. They took a passive stance and expected sensory impressions to impinge upon a nervous system, after which some perceptual connection would take place. Evidently, their epistemology required sociological assumptions. But this is evident only from knowing something about contemporary social psychology.

Mill's canons of causation. John Stuart Mill was concerned about proving cause. Probably his point of departure was his feeling that certain causes were indeed known. The problem in that case, is to develop formal proofs of their existence. Mill developed three canons, which he believed were sufficient to prove causality. There have been critics of these; foremost, for us, are Morris Cohen and Ernest Nagel.[8] Mill's canons follow.

a. *The Method of Agreement.* If two or more instances of the phenomenon under investigation have only one circumstance in common, the circumstance in which alone all instances agree, is the cause (or effect) of the given phenomenon.

b. *The Method of Difference.* If an instance in which the phenomenon under investigation occurs, and an instance in which it does not occur, have every circumstance in common save one, that one occurring in the former; the circumstances in which alone the two instances differ, is the effect, or the cause, or an indispensable part of the cause of the phenomenon.

c. *The Method of Concomitant Variation.* Whatever phenomenon varies in any manner whenever another phenomenon varies in some particular manner, is either a cause or an effect of this phenomenon, or is connected with it through some fact of causation.

It should perhaps be noted that each of these methods presupposes something different regarding the causal relation. The method of agreement presupposes knowledge of the consequent. It is therefore operationally related to observation and *ad hoc* analysis. The method of difference logically presupposes some knowledge of the antecedent and is therefore operationally related to the experimental design.

Now, the method of agreement seems acceptable at first glance. However, as Cohen and Nagel point out, this canon cannot be used as a device for *discovery* because it presupposes some technique by which one may select the relevant circumstances. Since the antecedent must be assumed to be present, the canon is inadequate for demonstration because it could lead to false conclusions. Moreover, observe the possible situation of multiple causation of the kind where more than one cause necessitates the effect. The method of agreement is hardly usable in such a case. What this method apparently provides is a technique for eliminating proposed causes. It merely asserts that nothing can be the cause of a phenomenon which is not a common circumstance in all instances of the phenomenon. Since our knowledge of the phenomenon requires propositions asserting membership in some class, this canon requires perfect methods of classification.

The method of difference is not much better off. Cohen and Nagel argue that two things render the method difficult. The assertion of "every circumstance" is a large order. To claim that this means only every *relevant* circumstance requires a criterion of relevancy which is not included in the canon. Again, a notion of perfect classification is required.

The method of concomitant variation is cleverly stated. Note, in particular, the point about being "connected . . . through some fact of causation." This clearly takes into account association; it would simply argue that association of two variables suggests an underlying connection. But this method is not without its faults. We have seen that how to distinguish between various kinds of association is an important issue—and this is not included in the canon. Thus, as Cohen and Nagel observe, this canon also presupposes knowledge not included in the canon. Unless one buys a causal monism, one may strain for the causal connection—how can one explain the correlation between the status of membership in certain English labor unions and the number of deaths in an Indian province? To be sure, statistical inference will permit the existence of a chance concomitant variation, but the canon does not. It may be insisted that most chance correlations fade on retest, and the canon specifies whenever—suggesting all possible situations; but one never has all possible situations, and this dodge fails us. All that can be affirmed from this canon is that A and C are not causally related if A and C do not vary concomitantly.

Induction in science. Formal logic of the sort encountered in the second chapter has been called deductive logic. One is given a set of premises. Then, according to rules agreed upon, one deduces subsequent conclusions. A hasty formulation held that in deductive logic one went from the general to the particular. This meant that general propositions formally necessitated certain (but not all) particular propositions. When one began with facts—or particulars—one wished to end up with generalizations. This was called induction.

The problem of induction was intimately connected with the search for causes. For in the quest for causality, one first observed particular events and then sought to explain them. One first observed things and then classified them. The question became How does one get classification? Some thought one found them in nature: a hippopotamus was so obviously a hippopotamus that no one could possibly misclassify the beast.

One famous kind of induction is mathematical induction. Bertrand Russell has shown that this is not really induction at all: The mathematician develops a set of rules which he agrees upon *prior* to any attempted proof. He then deduces consequences from these rules and calls these consequences induction.[9] We will not concern ourselves with this kind.

We must face up to two ideas of induction. One is called analytical induction by Florian Znaniecki;[10] the other is induction as it inheres in statistical reasoning.

We should perhaps recall when Znaniecki formulated his method. Although his *The Method of Sociology* was published in 1934, the con-

45

ceptualization apparently at least began during his work (1918–1920) on *The Polish Peasant in Europe and America* (published in 1927). The methodology of that work centered on the personal document; and though analytic induction holds no particular brief for that source of information, *The Polish Peasant* is an apologia in the case-study-versus-statistics polemics. My comments are not intended to defend the statistics with which Znaniecki jousted; a review of much research of that day must admittedly sustain his charge of toilet-counting and other kinds of pointless pebble-picking. The question is the acceptability of the case-study method.

Analytic induction requires the assessment of a number of cases. The task is to determine the proper classes to which the interesting cases belong. Beginning with the assumption that "any datum is already either A or non-A," Znaniecki offers the underpinnings in this contention:

Any object belongs to the class A only if it possesses all those fundamental characters which all other objects belonging to class A possess, and which are comprehended in the concept A.[11]

This is clearly related to Mill's canon of agreement. Now, according to Znaniecki, no definition of the class "precedes in analytic induction the selection of the data to be studied as representatives of this class."[12] One analyzes the data before any general formulation is made. One really need not worry about the size of the sample: for if the formulation is "well done, there is nothing more of importance to be learned about the class which these data represent by any subsequent investigation of more data of the same class."[13]

This obviously rejects the possibility of variation within the class. All members of a class are identical to all others. The phrase "more data of the same class" could be, of course, a question-begging caution. Any datum which does not conform to the class as "discovered" does not belong in that class, but in some other. For if it belonged in that class, it would behave as do all other members. *This denies the possibility of being wrong.* It is at least contrary to the mood of modern science which requires the scientist to assert, in advance, the conditions under which he will agree that his hypothesis must be rejected, as well as under which it will be accepted.

Although Znaniecki holds that his method is related to the type method (and there is a kinship with Becker's cultural case study method[14]) none of the sociologists who acknowledge allegiance to this method really has obeyed the injunction to wait until the data are all analyzed before asserting a class membership. They moreover all begin with some idea of the class they seek. In a formal discussion of analytic induction, William S. Robinson [15] cites Donald R. Cressey's use of the procedure. Essentially the steps are these: (1) the phenomenon is roughly defined; (2) a hypothesis is formulated; (3) one case is studied to see if the hypothesis fits all the cases; (4) if not, either the phenomenon is redefined to exclude the particular case or the hypothesis is modified; (5) the researcher continues until satisfied, remembering that a single negative instance is sufficient to throw the entire hypothesis out.

Robinson correctly points out that the idea of a working hypothesis is not unique to analytic induction. Robinson then uses a two-by-two table to illustrate the difference he finds between statistical inference and analytic induction. I quote at length.

Let C in Table 1 stand for instances in which these conditions are present, and $\sim$C for instances in which not all of them are present. Thus, the first row of the table contains instances in which the conditions C are present, and the second row contains instances in which not all of them are present.

Table 1

	P	$\sim$P
C	X	?
$\sim$C	0	X

As the method is described it consists in studying cases in the left column of Table 1 and then so defining C, the conditions, as to make all these cases fall in the upper cell of the column, as indicated by an X in the upper cell and the zero in the lower cell. We may go further, moreover, and point out that all of the cases in the lower row must fall in the right column. . . .

The relation between analytic induction and enumerative or statistical induction is now clear. A statistician would study cases in all four cells of the table. He would hope, but not insist, that there would be zeroes in the lower left and upper right cells—and there he would stop.

Robinson has properly shown the limitations of the so-called analytic induction method as it is related to a two-by-two table. However, as we shall see in Chapter 5 (p. 93), it is not necessary to hope for a zero in the righthand upper cell.

47

Other difficulties are present. Analytic induction is clearly an ad hoc solution to a given problem. As I indicated earlier, no test is permitted in the ad hoc analysis. Although all users of the method of analytic induction uniformly agree that contrary cases require some sort of modification, none seems to have observed that no kind of proof is contained in this method. Robinson sees the need for sampling: but he buys the requirement of zeros in the minor diagonal. Since these are empirical data, one can never assert zeros because all the cases are never in. The phenomenon may always yet require modification; the range of the hypothesis may yet be further limited. Since this condition seems to be built into the system, it is difficult to see that any kind of proof is contained in the argument. And therein lies an important difference, perhaps the significant point in the analytic-induction-versus-statistical-inference battle. The statistical technique can never be used to explain why a particular premise was considered. Properly used, the statistical technique tests premises, not discovers them. Conversely, analytic induction can never be regarded as proof. But it certainly provides a set of guides useful in the process of developing some hypothesis. When one looks at most introductory texts on research methods, one is struck by the absence of any comments on how to develop hypotheses. As we noted, there can be no rules for this, only vague guides. This is precisely what analytic induction provides. If one regards the scientist as a mere technician, a witless individual incapable of thought (or worse, whose thinking—being a subjective process—is dangerous because it is not capable of replication and must therefore be denied), there is no need to worry about the source of hypotheses. But if the scientist is creative, if that is, the generation of hypotheses is as scientific as their test, then analytic induction has much to offer.

This is particularly true in contemporary research. Many scientists are taught to have a problem, to have a theory, to have hypotheses (mainly null ones). Few of them have any appreciation of what their data will look like. Except for a blind reliance on some data-gathering technique, they know little about the content. It would seem that a thorough dose of analytic case studies would be immensely beneficial, if only to present the researcher with some idea of what the world is like.

As we have noted, this method was developed in answer to to an enumerative kind of statistics. Most textbooks today describe the techniques which Znaniecki combated as descriptive statistics. Inferential statistics, the deductive form that allows for inference in the case of a contradiction, was formalized later. The notions of range of confidence and Type I and Type II error, vital to the use of probability theory in substantive research, seem to be answers to the doubts that Znaniecki had. He asserts:

Unless he [the researcher] has actually investigated the majority of the data of a given class S, he cannot even affirm rightfully that most S are P; but only that "Some S are P." If he concludes from the latter to the former his judgment remains unreliable because somebody else may have investigated an equal or larger number of data and come forward with the claim that "most S are non-P."[16]

Although the awkward phrase "most S are non-P" reveals that he had no understanding of inferential statistics, the idea of confidence bands clearly encompasses the contingency of sample proportions varying from, say, 45 to 55 per cent. As a matter of fact, the skilled statistician could assert the probability of making such an error. But no matter; this is trivial. Of more consequence is the necessity not only to know the categories to be used and to modify them along the way, but to finally arrive at certainty. Neither errors of measurement nor sampling variations are permitted. This certainly is not possible with today's techniques. It is doubtful that it could ever be possible.

If Znaniecki should have welcomed probability statements, does this mean that statistical inference is inductive in character? R. A. Fisher says it is.[17] Hagood and Price concur,[18] although they observe that Einstein thinks all scientific reasoning is deductive. Part of the difficulty is semantic, part a real difference of orientation to research. The semantic difficulty lies in failing to distinguish between logic as formal argument and the process of research. Logical relations are simultaneous, immediate, and the only truth values permitted are true and false. Scientific relations are not immediate: a passage of time is required. Moreover, the scientist introduces a third truth-value, namely, doubtful. The adjudication of this doubt takes time. It results from a process. One must not confuse the atemporal structure of argument with the sequence of events consuming time in the scientific decision.

As a question of logic, induction fails miserably. The intent of induction is to enable one to discover something new. But logic involves progress from premise to conclusion; whatever is contained in the conclusion must be contained in the premises. But if it is in the premises, it is not new. Hence, induction is not, strictly speaking, logic; if it is not logic, it must be a process. Moreover, Francis and Golightly have demonstrated that any statistical equation can be shown to be a deductive argument.[19] Consider the argument that two means are different in the statistical sense of difference. What kind of argument is employed in reaching this conclusion? One develops a theoretical distribution of sample means based upon certain assumptions (randomness, independence, etc.). From the laws of probability, he deduces the likelihood of obtaining a statistic of a given magnitude. He sets up a syllogism of the form "If chance explains the differences between means, than .05 level of Type I error, my critical ratio will be less than 1.96. It is greater than 1.96 (this minor premise is demonstrated by his arithmetic, which is presumably correct). Hence I must reject the subject of my major premise—chance is not the explanation: the two means are really different." Hence statistical inference is, basically, deductive.

To recapitulate briefly: The question centered on the status of induction, and in particular on the position of statistical inference as a kind of induction. We recalled that logic and the research sequence differ in respect to time. Logic proceeds from the premise to the conclusion and hence cannot be used for discovery. Induction suggests but does not imply discovery: strictly speaking, it is not logic. It must, then, be a process. Moreover, any statistical equation is seen to be deductive. Hence it is logic and not induction. Hasty reading of this section may lead to confusion.

The point to be made is that the statistical equation is a special kind of formal deductive logic. But empirical research is part of a process: and there is nothing to say that the research process must not employ deductive logic. What has been called induction by statisticians turns out to be the process of empirical research by another name, and not, as suggested, a kind of logic. This requires us to consider a different orientation to the real world.

What happens, apparently, is that whatever their source, hypotheses are put in deductive form and tested accordingly. It does not matter formally where hypotheses come from. All that is required is that they be put in proper form for rigorous test. Although this may settle one aspect of the problem, it raises a number of issues.

One of the issues is concept formation. This is not merely a matter of formal consideration, nor can one assume a process of concept formation. This is a matter of substantive social science. Yet clearly various points of view are possible. These seem to be contingent upon one's position regarding a metaphysical issue: is nature continuous? Leibnitz said, "Nothing happens all at once, and it is one of my great maxims, and among the most completely verified, that *nature never makes leaps: Which I call the Law of Continuity.*"[20] At least consistent with this point of view is the doctrine that one learns concepts just as one learns anything else—by the reduction of error. A contrary point of view is that which is similar to Gestalt psychology—at critical times (perhaps under knowable conditions) the mind takes a leap and arrives at a concept. From this latter point of view, learning which name one should associate with the color yellow is different from apprehending that blocks, say, have *color* as well as shape, or exist in countable *number*. We will return to this issue in a moment. Now we must glance in another direction.

A second major issue, if induction is simply another name for empirical research, is that there are at least two distinguishable kinds of empirical research. Consider the possibility of measuring families in terms of their degree of authoritarian structure. We may proceed in two directions. On the one hand, we may seek to describe the family structures in, say, Minneapolis, Minnesota, in 1958. Statistically, we may be interested in identifying and measuring mean authoritarianism and the variance of authoritarianism. This is an empiricism bound to time and space. We may also propose the question of the relation between degree of authoritarian family structure and achieved status. We may have some hypothesis that requires achievement to be related to a democratic family structure and ascribed status to be related to the authoritarian family pattern. This does not require anyone to specify what the typical family in a given community is like. This kind of empiricism is of a different order than the former kind.

The distinction can be better discerned when the passage of time is differentially involved. Let us assume that marital adjustment is not instantaneous. Indeed, it is not likely to be an event in the sense of being achieved at some point in time. Adjustment probably is a process, and requires the passage of time. We will call this kind of time *process time*.

Another kind of time may be called *historical time*. Here the conditions that (say) cause adjustment or maladjustment may themselves change. Suppose that under conditions of economic expansion marital adjustment is facilitated and under conditions of economic depression adjustment is also facilitated; but movement from one condition to the other increases the likelihood of maladjustment. It is not likely that any society remains in a given condition for any appreciable length of time. Indeed, it may be true that before the process has had time to complete its course the historical conditions change, and a new relationship exists. Clearly, the statements about process time and historical time appeal to different kinds of evidence. The research process (itself being involved in historical time) must, somehow, take this into account.

Another dodge: necessary and sufficient conditions. Another way to release the pressure of the question How do you find causes? is to suggest that *cause* is a bad word. *Association* may also be labeled a bad word. A nice word is *conditions.*

Consider the set of conditions A and their negation ~A. We will understand that these conditions are the supposed antecedents of some interesting phenomenon. If, whenever we have the conditions we always have the consequent (which we denote by C), but may or may not have the consequent when the conditions are negated, we call them sufficient conditions.

$$A \qquad \sim A$$
$$C$$
$$\sim C \qquad 0$$

This formulation can take care of multiple causes in the first sense (i.e., many causes can each produce the given event). To determine the sufficiency of any alternative, we simply give it a turn as A. This formulation can also take care of multiple causes in the second sense. The antecedent condition may be completely or simply defined. Note that multiple causes in the first sense can never produce necessary conditions. That this is so is seen in the *definition* of necessary conditions. Necessary conditions require that the consequent never occurs when the antecedent is absent; for if the consequent could occur in such a case, the proposed one could hardly be necessary.

$$A \qquad \sim A$$
$$C \qquad 0$$
$$\sim C$$

It should come as no shock that the joint occurrence of these two sets of conditions should be known as necessary and sufficient:

$$
\begin{array}{ccc}
 & A & \sim A \\
C & & 0 \\
\sim C & 0 &
\end{array}
$$

One further possibility must be admitted. A and C may stand in one relation (e.g., sufficiency may exist) to each other under certain conditions, say B. But if the conditions change—say, to B_2 the relation between A and C changes (e.g., to necessity). This situation has been called joint effects and interaction. Since social scientists have already attached a meaning to the term interaction, rather than introduce any further ambiguity into sociology, we will use the perhaps more clumsy term joint effects.

It is probably safe to say that many people regard necessary and sufficient conditions as the desideratum of scientific inquiry. As will be explained later, I do not. Suffice it to say here that I feel it necessary to leave room for error. However, I point out that these various conditions are clearly related to logical forms. The tabular presentation of sufficiency is structurally that of implication. Thus, in the case of sufficient conditions, the antecedent *implies* the consequent. Necessity is seen to contain the relation of subimplication: the antecedent is implied by the consequent. The similarity of this to Mill's canons of agreement and difference is readily apparent. The joint occurrence of necessity and sufficiency is seen to involve the if-and-only-if relation. The purpose of this digression is to remind the reader that propositions about antecedent conditions are logically related to those about consequences.

It may appear to most that distinction between cause and association ought to have some implications here. Something like the following appears to be correct. In the case of association, one cannot distinguish between antecedents and consequences. But if the theory requires us to believe that one state of affairs is prior (either temporally or logically) to the other, the one which is prior to the other would be called the antecedent. Some word suggesting cause would probably not be out of order.

A proposed way out. Operationalism seems to assume the task of giving content to form. Induction assumed the task of giving form to content. The latter step seems to require a process, possibly a leap, in the formation of a concept. Asking where concepts come from is much like asking where hypotheses come from. When we refer to a specific item of content, the matter belongs to the sociology of science. And methodology does not ask where the hypothesis came from; this is not merely a matter of form—the hypothesis belongs to theory as well. No matter where the hypothesis comes from, it is a *proposed* solution to a problem. Methodology constitutes the rules of the game. If one performs according to the rules, then the decision he reaches is justified and proper. If the rules are broken, the decision, no matter how correct, is improper and cannot be allowed. As a matter of fact, the decision following from improper procedure is usually regarded as being incorrect in the sense that it is not accepted. It may be believed, but it is not known.

We still have not settled the issue of cause.

We must first try to determine what kind of error was made in the historical search for cause. We must admit that both Hume and Pearson thought that something like cause existed in the world of fact (sense impression). All that they really agreed to was that *cause could never be discovered because it could never be seen*: no sense impression of cause existed. A proper question is, why should one believe in ideas of cause and yet decide causes could never be discovered—could never be proved to exist?

The empirical critics of cause made the same error everyone else made. And they added one of their own. They assumed that cause was a *thing*, something that could be seen. When one looks at the ideas of necessary and sufficient conditions, and the possible modifications to the idea of association, one finds the clue. Cause is not a thing capable of causing impressions. Cause is a kind of relation between phenomena. But science deals with propositions about phenomena, not the things themselves. Accordingly, cause is a kind of relation between data statements. The historical error was in asking an improper question.

The question seemed proper because one could hardly believe in uncaused events. The rejection of uncaused seemed to require an affirmation of cause. Then, without examining the idea of *explanation*, one simply looked for things in the world called causes. This is like looking for *truths* in the real world of sense impression. Truths, like causes, are not things. A proposition may be true or false: the world is neither true nor false, it merely is. Truth is a judgment one makes about propositions.

Similarly, one ought not look for things called causes: one looks for particular kinds of relations and calls certain kinds causal and other kinds associational. Science must develop rules which will permit one inference or the other. The limiting feature is not so much the real world as it is the kind of statements we make about the real world. For example, if we are unable to assert a temporal relation between the occurrence of A and the subsequent occurrence of B, we would be unable to assert cause.

Instead of expending effort trying to describe the essence of cause—this is the real metaphysical trap—one ought to look at the idea of explanation, and the relation of data to theory. The historical position of induction (the position of the so-called empiricists) has been that one receives sensations from the real world and the mind organizes them in some habitual manner. One proceeded from fact to generalization. One first observed carefully and "objectively," and then one classified the things observed. After classification, one compared and then generalized. The generalization was an *abstraction* of particular things, comparison being necessary to insure against mixing two classes in the generalization.

In this way of thinking the observer was passive. Indeed, the effort was to develop techniques of observation (including measurement) that would be completely independent of the observer. Were this done, there would be no error; and the generalizations which necessarily follow from correct observations would truly be laws.

Let us assess this tremendous effort expended to achieve objectivity. What I now have to say may never have occurred to any empiricist of the old school. I offer it as being consistent with their beliefs. I am not basically interested in assessing personal motivation. Much difficulty has resulted from this insistence upon objectivity. It assumes a passive role on the part of the observer (the scientist). Indeed, there was no role for the scientist in science. Anyone armed with the right techniques could make proper observations. The generalizations could take care of themselves.

A confusion developed about the roles of the technician and the scientists. Scientists wrote books to instruct people how to work for them. When a sociologist, say, hires an interviewer, he wants the interviewer to behave as similarly to the sociologist as possible. He wishes to control any error introduced by hiring someone to act in his stead. As a matter of fact, he wishes that the error would drop dead ("approach zero" as mathematicians are wont to say). And I agree with this sort of thing: the technician who merely acts for the scientist ought to be mechanical; he ought to be merely another arm of the scientist.

It is not so much that we know this is not true, that error will always creep in. The error is in thinking that if one describes how a technician ought to act he is describing how a scientist ought to act. This is, basically, fallacious reasoning. The proper argument puts the scientist as the antecedent of the technician, not the converse. We must boldly assert another principle of research design. The scientist stands in an active relation to the world he seeks to explain. He is creative.

Instead of trying to develop rules by which a passive inert technician can discover something new (the contradictory promise of induction), one ought to develop rules for testing a proposed idea. The rules serve not as a source of hypotheses, but as guides to their acceptability. Logic will enable one to determine whether a person has argued correctly from his premises. Logic will be unable to tell a person which premises to consider. The introduction of a new idea, or a new combination of old ideas, is not a matter of logic. This is not the job of a passive technician, a living robot who does what he is told. This is the task of the scientist who is creative, who is actively related to this world of data.

One ought never confuse the logical sequence of an argument with the temporal sequence of the research process. In experimentation one tends to find a close correspondence between the structure of argument and the sequence of the experimental operations. The premise exists both in the argument and in the fact prior to the consequent. This is not always so. Sometimes the conclusion is really a set of data which the scientist seeks to explain; he then develops an ad hoc explanation of it. Naturally, I would agree that the ad hoc explanation does not constitute a test. The ad hoc explanation may account for the problematic data; but since it exists after the problem, there is no logical necessity for the connection. Later, the explanation may be part of the premise and tested to determine whether the same relation appears.

This allows us to say that, logically, theories (the concepts, the principles of relation, etc.) exist prior to their data. Temporally, this may not be so. But, given a theoretical position, one may deduce the consequent. One may attempt to recreate the conditions asserted as necessary in the theory and determine whether or not the consequent emerges in fact. If it does, this is taken to be a verification of the theory; failure

56

to achieve the consequent is taken as a falsification of the theory—or an inability to recreate the conditions necessary for the test.

We still have not decided what constitutes explanation. It is not likely that we will develop a completely satisfactory notion. Something akin to the statisticians' notion of reducing variance is required. In the case of quantitative data, this is like trying to achieve as great a correlation coefficient as possible. It is not exactly true to assert that one seeks a correlation coefficient equal to unity. One can achieve this whenever he desires. Consider a linear correlation between two measures: by introducing an increasing number of degrees of a parabolic equation, eventually one may completely account for variance. This is necessarily so: the straight line involves the first moment (essentially the mean); the second-degree parabola introduces the second moment (essentially variance); the third-degree parabola introduces the third moment, and so on. By introducing a sufficient number of moments, one may have a line without any scatter. It would be horribly complicated, and probably impossible of sensible interpretation. Occam's razor seems to be needed.

In the case of categorically defined data, this is tantamount to seeking that set of classes which results in probabilities of either unity or zero. This may require a separate class for each individual included in the study, especially in view of the inability of obtaining perfect classificatory operations. One would hardly epitomize science in this manner. It looks as though Occam's razor has another job.

Since, therefore, reduction of variance is not merely a technical problem, it must adhere to theory. Part of the connection may be found in terms of ideas about laws and generalization and fitted curves. Any set of data can be fitted to some line. This is built into the algebraic argument involved in the derivation of the constant terms. One may have found a number of similarly fitted lines—say, the relation of age at first marriage of husbands and wives. One may even predict obtaining a straight line and then obtain one from his data. This does not make it a law. By finding this relation in all conceivable situations, one may claim it to be a general relation. But it still is not a law. Until the constant terms are incorporated into theory in such a way that the relationship is a necessary consequence of the theory, we do not have a law.

Thus, one may find a particular kind of relation in his data. He still may ask How come? Whether or not this question demands "the operation called verstehen" depends upon what is admitted to theory. That is to say, whether or not explanation involves an assessment of the subjective status of the people being studied is a matter of theory, of what is accepted as premises of inquiry, not a point of view about science. Formally, methodology may demand replication to insure against error introduced by the private biases of the scientist; but it cannot tell the scientist what premises to consider. It can only tell him that a particular premise does not allow the inference he seeks to achieve.

A passive notion of the scientist is contrary to the idea of how to discover something new. A conception of the scientist as creative allows for the observation that some well-trained scientists are drones when it comes to producing new ideas and that others, perhaps less well trained, make startling contributions. Instead of dreaming of rules which try, in essence, to tell idiots how to act like geniuses, one should observe that the proper task of methodology is to provide means for testing ideas. Laws, instead of being things out in the real world, are principles of inference: deductions from them are tested to test the law itself. Theory is logically prior to the data. Hence, data which are contrary to theoretical expectations must be taken as falsification of the theory.

We now are able to discuss, intelligently, the problem of causes. Whatever cause means is a matter of metatheoretical concern in the same manner that laws are a matter of metatheory. Propositions defining causal relations may be admitted to theory; one does not "see" relations: one infers them from a body of rules. Deductions of subsequent behavior are then made and tested. If the behavior is that which was expected, one verifies the assertion of causal relation. If the behavior differs from what was expected, one denies the assertion of causality. Whether one must have certainty before one asserts causality is a matter of definition of a particular kind of relation.

Thus, causality, like other propositions of science, is put into deductive form and tested in the same way as other hypotheses. After all, if causality is a kind of relation, and a hypothesis is a proposed test of relation, there is no reason why one may not propose a hypothesis of causal relation. Earlier, we admitted a principle of errorful operational specification. This denies the ability to assert certainty. If, therefore, certainty is a necessary part of the idea cause, the latter idea must be abandoned. Unless, that is, one is willing to speak of probable cause. In any event, there are no rules for the discovery of causes. Statements about causes, if operational specifications are warranted, may be tested.

The similarity of this formulation and the role of prediction in science, discussed earlier, is apparent.

The two-by-two model. The two-by-two table is readily seen as a device for cross-tabulating frequencies associated with two dichotomies. The most general set of dichotomies is probably that related to antecedents and consequents. The dichotomy refers either to the presence or the absence of either the antecedent or the consequent. Thus we could have the table

$$A \qquad \sim A$$

$$C$$

$$\sim C$$

where A, $\sim A$, C and $\sim C$ have the meanings previously attached. The idea of certainty would require that at least one cell be zero.

This schema borrows heavily from the laboratory sciences. The notion of an antecedent is especially happy in the case of an experiment in chemistry. For that reason, we must observe at least three conditions defining the antecedental dichotomy. Parallel conditions exist for the consequent.

$A = A \cdot \sim A$. This is the classical condition. The "not A," or absence of the proposed antecedent, is primitively defined. Then the condition defining A is added to the "not A" condition. For example, we may have "not A" stand for pure water; then A could be salt. The question to be answered, "Does the addition of salt to pure water result in the interesting consequent?

$\sim A = \sim (A) \cdot B$. This represents a frequent situation in the social sciences, especially in those that get their data from surveys. The condition defining A is falsified and some other condition than A is present. Suppose one wishes to explain the achievement of success in grade school teaching (however success may be measured). For the antecedents, one may entertain the idea of classifying teachers according to whether they have graduated from a teachers' college or from a state university. Now "teachers' college" is not merely something added to a "not teachers' college" condition. Nor is "state university" simply a negation of "teachers' college." Many alternatives exist in the negation of "teachers' college."

$\sim A = (\sim A) \cdot B \cdot C \cdot D \ldots$ This is, essentially, an extension of the above condition. The major difference is that several alternatives exist in the case of $\sim A$. To continue the example, $\sim A$ may well include any other training than teachers' college—private liberal arts college as well as state university, or any mixture of training experiences. Anytime one has a quantitatively defined variable which is to be dichotomized, some form of the third alternative will be involved.

Quite possibly the most overlooked necessity in this usage of the two-by-two table is the requirement that the classifications recur.[21] "One swallow maketh not summer"; nor does one successful case prove a relation. The two-by-two table incorporating cross-tabulated frequencies, required the assumption of a repetitive event. It may appear that an operation of the order teachers' college graduate may be simple and shown easily to recur. As a data-statement grounded completely in space and time, the operation may be quite successful. But insofar as it is supposed to measure something sociologically relevant, the operation may be only moderately successful.

In developing a theory about political behavior, to change the example, one may use as an antecedent "intend to vote for Mr. Stevenson." This is not a recurring category; it is located in a time-space matrix. Yet it may be proposed as a measure of a recurring event, say, "liberal candidates." How—in what sense—"intend to vote for Mr. Stevenson" may be regarded as a uniform measure of liberality may be subject to dispute. Certainly some nonliberals intended to vote for him. That the candidacy of a particular person is an imperfect measure of some theoretical dimension must be admitted. The display of argument during a political convention suggests that the candidacy of, say, Kefauver, was measuring something that the candidacy of Stevenson was not. Which of the two was a better measure of a recurring category is not for us here to decide. We need only conclude that the designation of antecedent conditions is not a simple matter; and, in particular, a naive operational argument does not solve the problem.

We agreed that more than one successful case is necessary before one could properly conclude that a relation existed. Since repetition means not only recurrence in time but recurrence at any given moment in time, two questions arise. First, how many cases must one assess before one affirms the existence of an interesting relation? Second, what do we do with cases that do not conform to the expected pattern: how many failures are required before one admits that the proposed hypothesis has failed?

If we require certainty, then we probably can never reach a decision.

PROBLEMS IN THE PROOF OF CAUSALITY

To reach a decision, under the requirements of certainty, is to demand an inspection of all possible cases. Except in trivial areas, this is not likely ever to occur. As Hume observed, any proposition of empirical content has at least one reasonable alternative: "The sun will not rise tomorrow" is just as reasonable as "The sun will rise tomorrow." Certainty can never be achieved, since future cases could prove to be contrary to past experience.

Moreover, the principle of errorful measurement requires us to speak in probability terms. Instead of requiring a cell in our paradigm to equal zero, we will simply require it to approach zero. Just how many cases are needed to arrive at a decision will depend upon one's willingness to make either of science's two possible errors. It is quite apparent that some formal attention must be paid to the issue of probability and probability inference.

61

CHAPTER 4

The Rejection of Chance

THAT some formal attention to a theory of probability is required must be acknowledged. This follows from various considerations. Particular propositions—those about "some"—cannot provide the basis for a rigorous argument in traditional categorical logic. As a matter of fact, most of the propositions of the social sciences are of this sort; hence some logic in addition to a categorical one must be appealed to. As a matter of principle, I have taken the position that it is ultimately impossible to achieve error-free operational specifications for assigning class membership. If this is so, we can never achieve data statements in a form useful for categorical argument.

As with many terms employed in science, the term probability comes laden with common-sense overtones. Fortunately, most people are more likely to use the term probable than probability. It is not uncommon for people to employ such usages as "that is highly improbable"; "that is quite probable"; "that will probably happen." In one sense, perhaps, these formulations are analogous to such qualitative descriptions as hot, tepid, cold, and the like in measuring heat. Certainly many people associate "probable" with some feeling of uncertainty. I am unable to accept such a notion of probability. To use an earlier distinction, this sort of thing is appropriate to belief and we are seeking after knowledge.

An idea similar to the psychological uncertainty conception of probability is the so-called ignorance school. The famous philosophers, mathematicians, and statisticians (at least one whom I shall name can properly be called all three) who ascribed to this doctrine constitute an important roll in the history of western thought. Certainly Laplace, Bernoulli, Hume, and Mill, to name but a few, felt that if we really knew all there was to know about our data we would not have to use such unfortunate terms as probability. The idea still has currency, and some merit.

The traditional definition of probability went something like this: If an event can succeed in s ways and fail in f ways, all equally possible, then the probability that the event will succeed is given by

$$p = \frac{s}{s + f} \tag{4.1}$$

This seems like defining probability in terms of possibility, where possibility is a synonym for probability. Although this may describe one kind of probability, it cannot be considered a definition, because it is circular. Some alternative way must be available.

Before considering some alternatives, we should pay some attention to the terms possible and probable. Whatever may have been their meanings in other arguments, I find the following distinction useful. The notion of possibility inheres in theoretical definitions uniquely. There are only two conditions of possibility: the possible and the impossible. These are not matters of fact. These are matters of theory. The fact that no one has ever seen a unicorn does not mean that we never shall, that such a beast is impossible. But the assumed correctness of contemporary biological theory denies the possibility of its existence. Because this kind of animal contradicts what is accepted in theory, we say it is impossible. The existence of just one, or the proof that one did exist, would, of course, falsify the theory. Let us not imagine that theory can never be wrong. It most certainly can; and, when shown to be wrong, a problem exists: to identify the faulty proposition and remove it in favor of an acceptable one. Moreover, it is theoretically correct to assert that an animal (say) is possible, even if one has never been known to exist, if such is consistent with acceptable theory. Probability is another matter. Thus, in the succeeding pages, when the term possibility is used, various outcomes may all be possible, with different probabilities attached. The phrase "equally possible" is simply a redundancy. If an outcome is consistent with theory, it is consistent with theory. This is not a matter of magnitude.

63

Some basic ideas of probability. An example of the circularity of most mathematical definitions of probability can be found in J. V. Uspensky's *Introduction to Mathematical Probability*. He writes: "If, consistent with conditions S, there are n exhaustive, mutually exclusive, and equally likely cases, and m of them are favorable to an event A, then the mathematical probability of A is defined as the ratio m/n."[1] The phrase "equally likely" is clearly an appeal to some notion of probability. Some may object to this definition because it is restricted to equally likely cases, and it is apparently inappropriate in a case of unequally likely cases. One may develop a fairly decent rationale for assuming that all faces on a true die are equally likely to turn up. But suppose that one face has a greater likelihood of turning up than the rest: does this mean that probability theory is useless? Actually, it will turn out that this is not so. Yet we must admit that equally likely cases can represent a particular kind of probability. This can be highly useful since we may make this assumption and deduce consequences from it. Upon comparison with the world of fact, we may have to reject the assumption of equally likely cases. For the moment, we should leave the mathematical statistician hopefully considering his definition.

A statistical definition has been offered by Richard von Mises.[2] His contention is that one must define probabilities in terms of a random sampling operation. This is no great surprise; philosophically, he was an operationalist and tended to prefer operational definitions. His formulation has its advantages. With it, he can take into account unequal cases. Instead of having a simple ratio m/n, he would require a fancier one. He would also have a ratio of the favorable cases—denoted by f— to the total number n. But he would require this to approach a limit as n became infinitely large. Symbolically,

$$\lim_{n \to \infty} \frac{f}{n} = p \qquad (4.2)$$

and f/n may be taken as an estimate of p. It must be understood that this limit is not the kind associated with series encountered in high school mathematics. One may think of associating limit with something like $n + 1/n$. In this case

$$\lim_{n \to \infty} \frac{n+1}{n} = \lim_{n \to \infty} \frac{n}{n} + \lim_{n \to \infty} \frac{1}{n} = \lim_{n \to \infty} 1 + 0 = 1 \qquad (4.3)$$

With this in mind, one may suspect that when n gets infinitely large probability must always approach zero. This is not true: the idea of limit is akin to that involved in defining the limit of the ratio of the increment in y to the increment in x:

$$\lim_{\Delta x \to 0} \frac{\Delta y}{\Delta x} = \frac{dy}{dx}$$

(4.4)

In such a case, the numerator may or may not approach zero when Δx does; the limit applies to the *ratio*. Moreover, the limit of probability is not approached from either the right or the left but from both, as with a dial pointer fluttering around the true reading.

But even this limit was insufficient for von Mises. He distinguished between chance and probability, requiring the latter to contain randomness. Suppose one had the series

0, 1, 0, 1, 0, 1, 0, 1, 0, 1, 0, 1, 0, 1, 0, 1, 0, 1, 0, . . .

The limit of the ratios of the number of 1's to the total number would seem to be 1/2. But this depends entirely upon how the sample was taken—the place selection, to use his term. If one chose every odd case, this limit would appear to be zero; if one chose every even case, the limit would appear to be unity. A random series was required; a random series was one whose limit would appear unchanged regardless of the type of place selection.[3] Here random means uncertain, and a bit of circularity is still retained. From this restriction, it is commonly held that a mechanically produced series (i.e., a series of numbers resulting from a formula) is not random, but fixed. Chance may be appealed to when discussing those nonrandom situations; but probability must flow from a random series. A trivial criticism is that von Mises apparently forgot that one could have a random sampling operation in terms of which one could create a random series from the example of alternating zeros and ones. The reason he forgot is simple: he was using operations to define his world, which he called a sample space.

As a matter of fact, von Mises' idea of the sample space proved to be a major link in the development of modern statistical theory.[4] The linkage is to that branch of mathematics known as measure theory. And this ought to provide us with a clue: what the mathematical definition and the statistical definition of probability have provided is a *measurement of probability*. They have not improved any on our knowledge of what

65

probability is. If one seeks some quality of a thing called probability, one is seeking the unobtainable.

Just as it was improper to look for a thing called truth or cause, so it is improper to look for a thing called probability. One should recall that the importance of probability theory lies in the inability of categorical logic to build rigorous arguments on particular propositions. These were of the form "Some S are P." Probability is simply the measurement of the "someness" contained in the particular proposition. In order to develop knowledge of this, one must develop rules by which statements of this sort may be defended. What this really suggests is that probability is a primitive concept.[5]

The significance of creating a sample space, in the sense in which von Mises, William Feller, and others use the term, is in the ease with which appropriate operational specifications are possible. Thus, the mathematician's requirement of equally likely can be regarded as a sampling requirement—that each case of the universe has an equal chance of being included in the study or hypothesis to be tested. The requirement of randomness (in at least the sampling operation if not in the real world) allows for a feeling that the probability assigned to a class is true for all members of that class. This is not trivial.

The limits of statistical inference: Tchebycheff Inequality. One claim of statistical inference is that it can account for, and, indeed, measure error and the likelihood of error. It probably is not necessary to define what probability is any more than asserting something about its measurement of the someness of a particular proposition. We do not have to know what probability is associated with any particular outcome. All we need know is that *some* probability can be attached to an outcome of interest. It is the task of statistics to provide us with a measure of that probability. In the enlightened mood of statistical inference, one may estimate the probability of correctly asserting the probability in question.

This marvelous accomplishment is due to what is sometimes called the weak law of large numbers. An alias is the first law of large numbers, and the familiar name is Tchebycheff Inequality. To understand it, one must have some knowledge of probability distribution. An elementary knowledge of the normal curve, such as is given in any introductory course, is sufficient; however, the law does not depend upon a normal distribution. All one needs to know is that the more a given statistic deviates from the mean of a distribution as measured in standard deviation units, the rarer the event. Thus, something 5 S.D. units away from its mean is quite rare; something 50 S.D. units away is much rarer. It would be difficult to measure exactly or even approximately how rare it is. One should remember that the square of the standard deviation is variance. We will denote variance by V^2 and standard deviation by V.

In the following discussion[6] we will assume that $f(x)$ is a continuous distribution function with a *finite* variance. The reader who is uncomfortable with the mathematical symbols may prefer to read the material between the mathematical comments.

The problem is to determine what the probability is that a variable x will take on a value more than x t standard deviations away from its mean. Using integral notation—because of the assumed continuity of $f(x)$—the variance is defined as follows:

$$V^2 = \int_a^b (x - M)^2 f(x) dx$$

(4.5)

Now, the righthand member can be shown as the sum of a number of integrals provided that the limits are such that continuity is retained. What we want to do is to separate out a range around the mean tV units on either side. The following is simply a notational accounting of this.

$$V^2 = \int_a^{M - tV} (x - M)^2 f(x) dx + \int_{M - tV}^{M + tV} (x - M)^2 f(x) dx +$$

$$\int_{M + tV}^b (x - M)^2 f(x) dx$$

(4.6)

As long as t equals zero, the middle integral is at least never negative. That is, it must always equal zero or more. Hence,

$$V^2 \geqq \int_a^{M - tV} (x - M)^2 f(x) dx + \int_{M + tV}^b (x - M)^2 f(x) dx$$

(4.7)

Note the similarity of these integrals. The essential difference is in the designation of the limits. The upper limit of the lefthand integral is nearer the mean than is the lower limit; conversely, the lower limit of the righthand integral is closer to the mean than its upper limit. In each case, the quantity $(x - M)^2$ will take on its minimum value for that limit of integration nearest the mean. For the first integral, t is the upper limit; for the second it is the lower limit. Thus

$$V^2 \geq \int_a^{M-tV} (tV)^2 f(x)\,dx + \int_{M+tV}^b (tV)^2 f(x)\,dx$$

$$V^2 \geq (tV)^2 \left[\int_{M-tV}^a f(x)\,dx + \int_{M+tV}^b f(x)\,dx \right] \tag{4.8}$$

Here the first integral gives the probability that x will be to the left of $(M-tV)$, and the second that x will be to the right of $(M+tV)$. If we ask only for the probability that $x - M$ will be tV units from the mean, we are essentially asking that the algebraic signs be ignored. Thus, the bracketed sum of the two integrals gives the probability that the absolute difference $x - M$ is greater than tV—that x is more than tV units from the mean in either direction. Symbolically that would be given as

$$V^2 \geq t^2 V^2 \, P\left[|x - M| > tV \right] \tag{4.9}$$

Dividing out V^2 we obtain Tchebycheff Inequality:

$$P\left[|x - M| > tV \right] \leq \frac{1}{t^2} \tag{4.10}$$

This asserts that the probability that x is greater than t standard deviation units from the mean is less than the reciprocal of t^2. Note that we did not assume any form for $f(x)$. This is a completely general argument, subject only to the conditions cited earlier.

The real issue was to determine how appropriate sampling theory is in measuring probabilities. Then, we would let f/n, our sample estimate of probability, replace x in 4.10, and p, the true probability, replace M in 4.10. In this case, $V = \sqrt{pq/n}$. By substitution, 4.10 becomes

$$P\left[\left| \frac{f}{n} - p \right| > t \sqrt{\frac{pq}{n}} \right] \leq \frac{1}{t^2} \tag{4.11}$$

Now choose a number e greater than zero, but as small as desired. Then we may let t equal e/V. Upon substitution, 4.11 becomes

$$P\left[\left| \frac{f}{n} - p \right| > e \right] \leq \frac{pq \cdot 1}{e^2 \cdot n} \tag{4.12}$$

This is truly an interesting result. No matter how small e may be, since

pq is a finite number less than one, one may choose an n sufficiently large to make P be as small as possible. That is to say, for any e, there is a sample size n such that

$$P\left[\left|\lim_{n \to \infty} \frac{f}{n} - p\right| \to 0 \right] \to 1 \qquad (4.13)$$

This is the law of large numbers. The law may be read: under conditions of random sampling, it is possible to choose a sample size such that the difference between the estimated and true probabilities approaches zero with a probability approaching unity. From this law, we may accept the argument that a random sampling operation will enable one properly to measure probabilities to any given accuracy.

Some basic operations on probabilities. If we are convinced that random sampling procedures permit accurate measurements of probabilities, it is probably appropriate to determine what kind of inferences are possible, given certain probability statements. We will call an event with a set of alternatives such that a probability is associated with each alternative a probability system.

Under the condition that one of the outcomes must occur, we note that the sum of probabilities associated with the entire range of alternatives must equal unity. This provides us with a clue.

Rule 1. Given a probability system, with a set of alternatives, A_1, A_2, A_3, . . . A_n, the probability that, say, outcome A_1 or A_2 will occur is the sum of the two probabilities.

Let us consider a set of objects each of which participates in a number of probability systems. The objects may be human. One probability system may involve age categories, another probability system may involve voting preference, and so on. One may ask the question: what is the probability that an object will be in both alternative 1 of the age-set and (say) alternative 1 of the voting preference-set? This requires another argument.

Rule 2. Given an object which participates in a number of probability systems; if these probabilities are independent, then the probability that the object will participate in a specified outcome of the first system and a specified outcome of the second system, is equal to the product of these outcomes.

The second rule for combining probabilities has generated a probability syllogism.[7] Putting the argument into syllogistic form has some interesting consequences. An unimportant one is to remind users of statistics that their arguments are based on traditional logic. An important one will be disclosed. The probability syllogism has the following form:

PREMISE 1: The probability of outcome a is p_1.
PREMISE 2: The probability of outcome b is p_2.
PREMISE 3: The two probability systems are independent.
CONCLUSION: The joint probability of $a \cdot b$ is $p_1 p_2$.

The first two premises are (essentially) established through sampling procedures. The universe which one samples contains the member of the *subject* error of the proposition offered. The third premise is not merely a formal assumption. It contains an assertion about the real world. It may be true or false: until an appropriate test is made, it is in doubt. Some statisticians prefer to define independence as a condition such that the joint probability is equal to the product of the two probabilities. This makes a perfect tautology. The point is not to complain about tautologies. Some are necessary. Our point is to look elsewhere.

Earlier, we observed that a particular proposition generated a probability statement. Indeed, the someness of the particular proposition is measured by probabilities. Consider these statements:

a. Some A is C.
b. The probability of an A being C is p.

These seem to be equivalent assertions, except for the precision of b. A closer look at a will suggest a problem. The statement form is made up of three parts: a subject (A), a predicate (C), and a copula (is). Statement b attaches the probability to the copula. When the theory of probability was an ignorance theory, one could say that there was some reservation about copulating or joining the subject and the predicate. In other words, statement-form b is consistent with an ignorance theory of probability.

Another formulation is possible. One might assert

c. All A's have a probability, p, of being C.

The predicate term is changed: it is now a class of objects having a p probability of being C. Here the element of doubt is removed. There is no appeal to ignorance or to psychological uncertainty. As a matter of fact, it is no longer a particular proposition but a universal one. Of course, it may be false if only some A's have the required probability, or if none of them does, and p is only an average probability. The statement is also false if lack of independence is shown; the lack of independence implies that the asserted p is not true for some cases. Let us now develop a probability syllogism containing propositions of this kind. The interesting thing about form c is that it enables one to drop the premise of independence. Thus one may argue

PREMISE 1: All A have a p_1 probability of being a.
PREMISE 2: All A have a p_2 probability of being b.
PREMISE 3: All A have a p_1p_2 probability of being both a and b.

This condition is completely consistent with original data in universal proposition form. In that case one could argue:

PREMISE 1: All A have 1.00 probability of being a.
PREMISE 2: All A have 1.00 probability of being b.
CONCLUSION: All A have a 1.00 probability of being both a and b, since $1 \times 1 = 1$.

Perhaps this situation seems unimportant. But the fact that independence warrants universal propositions is indeed important. For from this we may set up the rule that one introduces more and more controls until one reaches a relation of independence. When this is reached, one has achieved universal propositions regarding membership in classes having known probabilities of occurring.

It is evident that the condition of independence is an important one. And any test for independence is of fundamental consequence to theory-building.

The exact probability test. Before proceeding to a discussion of an exact test of probabilities, two things are in order. First, one should recall that before a logical relation other than independence is to be asserted, independence must be tested. Second, a given arrangement of items may occur with a very small probability. But, when one knows that the particular arrangement may occur a great number of times, the probability that one of them shall occur can be considerable. This follows from the first rule of combining probabilities. Some method for measuring the ways an interesting arrangement may occur is required.

McCormick cites the following algebraic operation as a theorem. "If an event A can occur in m ways, and thereafter an event B can occur in n ways, A and B can occur together in the order named mn ways."[8] This theorem, it should be noted, becomes the basis for permutations and combinations. Suppose that one has events A, B, . . . N; and suppose that N can occur n ways, M can occur $n - 1$ ways, etc., back to A occurring $n - n + 1$ ways. According to the theorem, the events can jointly occur the product of the various ways they could occur. Symbolically, this would require the factorial notation: the events $A, B, \ldots N$ could occur in n! ways.

Sometimes our inquiry is concerned with various arrangements of subsets of the sample set, as well as with the various arrangements of the total sample set. Given a sample of n objects, in how many ways can you obtain S successes, if each case is equally likely? To answer this question, the matter of order *within* the problematic arrangement must be decided. That is, one must decide whether order is or is not relevant to the analysis.[9]

Suppose that a typical undergraduate social action group must elect a president, a treasurer, and a secretary out of n members. There is a rule which says that no member can hold more than one office. Clearly, there are n ways to elect the first officer; $n - 1$ to elect the second; and $n - 2$ ways to elect the third. Accordingly, this social action group could elect (n) $(n - 1)$ $(n - 2)$ permutations of officers. With n fairly large for undergraduate social action groups—anything, say, over 5—they could elect officers at each meeting and keep themselves busy for a whole academic year without repeating a slate of officers. When order is important, the arrangement is called a *permutation*.

Now, suppose that this social action group intends to practice their version of collective leadership. Under these rules, they simply seek to elect a three-man committee to take over collectively the officer roles. Whereas, the first arrangement differentiated between John as president, Jim as treasurer, and George as secretary, the second one does not. That is, the sequence of election is immaterial: John, Jim, and George is the same collective leader as Jim, John, and George. To determine the number of *combinations* (an arrangement where order is irrelevant), one must divide out the number of ways in which the subset itself may be arranged. This is, if the subset consists of S members, $S!$.

To compute the number of arrangements, with order regarded as important, one calculates the permutations. Let r denote the size of the interesting subset, and n the size of the set including the interesting subset. The number of permutations is found by the formula:

$$P(n, r) = \frac{n!}{(n - r)!}$$

(4.14)

To compute the number of arrangements with order regarded as unimportant, one calculates the number of combinations. With the same symbols, the number of combinations is found by the formula:

$$C(n, r) = \frac{P(n,r)}{r!} = \frac{n!}{r!(n-r)!} \qquad (4.15)$$

We now have sufficient information to enable us to determine the probability of obtaining a set of data contained in a two-by-two table. We will consider the general situation first.

Define the two-by-two table as

$$
\begin{array}{ccc}
& A & \sim A \\
C & a & b \quad n_1. \\
\sim C & c & d \quad n_2. \\
& n_{.1} & n_{.2} \quad N
\end{array}
$$

where n_1 is the sum of a and b; n_2 is the sum of c and d; $n_{.1}$ is the sum of a and c; and $n_{.2}$ is the sum of b and d. $n_1. + n_2. = N$. Clearly, the number of combinations of C is found by substituting N for n, $n_1.$ for r, and $n_2.$ for $n - r$ in 4.15. That is to say, the total number of arrangements generating the number classified as C is found by

$$\frac{N!}{n_1.!n_2.!} \qquad (4.16)$$

To get the number of successes—those arrangements which represent the internal distribution of the table, we need to determine the combination of C's for the number of A's and for the number of $\sim A$'s. By appropriate substitution in 4.15 the A's can occur in $n_{.2}!/b!d!$ ways; the $\sim A$'s can occur in $n_{.1}!/a!c!$ ways. Therefore, by our theorem, A and $\sim A$ can occur in $n_{.2}!/b!d!$ ways, and, using the same theorem, A and $\sim A$ can occur in the following number of ways:

$$\left(\frac{n_{.1}!}{a!c!}\right)\left(\frac{n_{.2}!}{b!d!}\right) \qquad (4.17)$$

Recurring to Uspensky's mathematical definition of probability, we note that we must obtain the ratio of the successful ways an event can occur to the total number of ways it can occur. Accordingly, we must

73

obtain the ratio of 4.17 to 4.16. Hence, for the probability of obtaining any given cross-tabulation in a two-by-two table, we may calculate

$$P_g = \frac{\left(\dfrac{n_{.1}!}{a!c!}\right)\left(\dfrac{n_{.2}!}{b!d!}\right)}{\dfrac{N!}{n_1.!\,n_2.!}} = \frac{n_{.1}!\ n_{.2}!\ n_1.!\ n_2.!}{N!a!b!c!d!} \qquad (4.18)$$

This is often referred to as Fisher's exact probability test.[10]

In the event that none of the cells equals zero, the rejection of chance must include the probability not only of the given distribution but of any more extreme one. This is done by calculating the probability for each distribution determined by (a) holding the marginals constant and (b) successively subtracting 1 from the smallest cell frequency until a P_g is calculated for some distribution containing a zero cell. According to the first rule of probabilities, the probability of obtaining a given distribution or a more extreme one is found by summing the separate probabilities.

To illustrate the techniques: consider the following distribution.

	A	~A	t
C	8	5	13
~C	4	1	5
t	12	6	18

Here:

$a = 8$	$b = 5$	$N = 18$
$c = 4$	$d = 1$	$n_1. = 13$
$n_{.1} = 12$	$n_{.2} = 6$	$n_2. = 5$

Substituting in 4.18 we get

$$\frac{13!12!6!5!}{18!8!5!4!1!} = \frac{165}{476} = .35 \text{ approximately} \qquad (4.19)$$

We must now compute the probabilities for the distribution

	A	~A	t
C	7	6	13
~C	5	0	5
t	12	6	18

Note that the marginals are the same as before and that the smallest frequency has been reduced by one. Because this distribution has a null cell, it is the last one to compute. Substituting the proper data in 4.18 we get

$$\frac{13!12!6!5!}{18!7!5!6!0!} = \frac{11}{119} = .09 \text{ approximately} \tag{4.20}$$

Accordingly, the probability of obtaining a distribution like the one in the original table or more extreme is the sum of these probabilities, approximately .44. This means that a distribution of the kind we had could occur by chance about forty-four times in a hundred. Most researchers would feel that they had been unable to disprove chance. Not that chance has been demonstrated; it is, however, completely consistent with the data.

It doesn't take a mathematical genius to see that 4.18 can require a very large amount of work if the smallest cell value is only a little larger—say around four or five members. However, the results can be obtained rather simply by the use of logs. For simplicity in notation, let us redesignate the items in the two-by-two table:

$$
\begin{array}{ccc}
 & A & \sim A & t \\
C & c_1 & c_2 & m_1 \\
\sim C & c_3 & c_4 & m_2 \\
t & m_3 & m_4 & \\
\end{array}
$$

Here c is cell value and m is marginal total. The log of 4.18 would be as follows:

$$\log P_g = \sum_{j=1}^{4} \log (m_j!) - \log (N!) - \sum_{k=1}^{4} \log (c_k!) \tag{4.21}$$

To obtain the probability of a given distribution, we let the frequency of the smallest cell (c_s) be denoted by a. Then, to obtain the probability sought, we obtain the anti-logs for all computations of 4.21 for the distributions of $c_s = a$ to $c_s = 0$.

For those who tend to be a bit careless, a caution is in order: always remember that 4.21 gives the logs of the probabilities. One must obtain the anti-log of 4.21 for each distribution before adding. If the results of 4.21 were added before the anti-log was obtained, one would have multiplied rather than added the probabilities. (See p. 179 for appendix giving the logs of n! for n = 1 to n = 100.)

One must always ask Under what condition am I justified in rejecting chance as an explanation? There are no rules for answering this question contained in the definition of probabilities. The procedure, however, is to say that the rare probability may be the basis for the rejection of chance. Thus, if a distribution (or a more extreme one) could occur only once in a thousand times by chance, then, if one rejected chance, he would be wrong once in a thousand. "That ain't so bad," statisticians chortle (few getting such rarities); "reject chance—the odds are with you."

Exactly when the odds are for and when they are agin the researcher is not easily determined. Tradition has it that (a) psychologists like to use the once-in-a-hundred rule and (b) sociologists like to use the once-in-twenty rule, although both prefer the once-in-a-thousand situation. "Rigorous" researchers have developed a pattern of announcing the significance level for each test, leaving the reader the option. "Faint heart ne'er won fair lady," nor did "rigor" win much more than "mortis."

Except for the fact that the idea cannot be measured, something like the following ought to be involved in setting the proper acceptance limits. If accepting the hypothesis alternative to chance requires more of a modification of theory than acceptance of the chance hypothesis, put the price ticket high. If the acceptance of the hypothesis requires little modification—if the theory can afford to contain a false hypothesis without too much disturbance—then put the price lower. Just how one should measure significance to theory is not known. For some reason, I suspect that this is a theoretical and not merely technical issue. Perhaps that is the reason it has no contemporary solution.

Statisticians often find it necessary to estimate probabilities. The current vogue is to estimate intervals rather than to essay point estimations. Nonetheless, they may, at some point in a study, assert that "the probability for this event is .38 ± 0.078"; and then go on to assert the probability for the truth of this statement. The statistical novice could excusably blanch. Yet the confusion can be clarified easily.

In the first place, a probability involving an empirical ratio of the f/n sort is a special case of the mean. This can be seen by assigning 1 to each favorable outcome and 0 to all others. Then the probability figure can be determined by appealing to the formula for the mean. Hence one should be prepared to see that the two probabilities are computed differently.

In the second place, the probability of the event—whatever was being estimated—is contained in a proposition about the world. The probability contained in the next part of the statement involves a proposition about a proposition. It flows from the premises of statistical or (if you will) probability theory. If the theoretical argument is accepted, the truth of this statement necessarily follows. We may observe then, that the second probability is not computed in the empirical sense; it is, strictly speaking, *deduced* from a theory. It is true that some arithmetic computation is involved, but its connection with the real world is of a different order than the ratio measure of probability.

The chi-square test. Except for those addicted to analytic induction (who wouldn't be caught dead using a probabilistic argument), most researchers avoid a study whose sample size is such that the exact probability can be easily computed. Even 4.21 can become a chore. Accordingly, a substitute formula has been sought and found. We can score this a victory for technique. Nothing new, theoretically, is added or taken away.

We should not imagine that this formula is simply a surrender to technique. The justification of the use of chi-square (and, by implication, the critical ratio of proportions) does not result from any arbitrariness on the part of statisticians. Barnard and Pearson independently worked on the problem of significance tests for two-by-two tables.[11] They posed three problems, each resting on different assumptions about probabilities, each generating different distributions of the probabilities. I have tacitly assumed that the marginal totals are proper estimates of probabilities and, as a matter of fact, pose no issue relating to their own distribution.

Fisher's exact method, which I have given above, is analogous to random assignment of two groups of individuals to two experimental conditions. We are simply observing the presence or absence of a particular reaction. Here the marginal totals are a function of the internal distribution and do not represent the results of a sample distribution. But suppose that we are interested in determining the difference of proportions in two random samples. Pearson, in the cited argument, first gives a binomial approximation of the hypergeometric probability involved in the solution of the problem. He then proposes a "normal" approximation to the binomial approximation. I shall utilize this fact in the next chapter to justify the algebraic manipulation showing the relation between the critical ratio of proportions and chi-square for the two-by-two table.

The third problem involves the selection of N individuals; a particular random process is hypothesized. In this process, individuals are classified into the four possible cells. This implies that both marginal totals may vary by the random process. Here, Pearson shows, we find that the solution of the statistical problem involves two binomial and one hypergeometric estimations. He then shows that a safe technique is the formula for the two-by-two table given earlier. By "safe" is meant that (if the marginals are not too small) the formal level of the probability of acceptance is likely to be much above the true chance of falling beyond that level. This is the same as requiring a higher than normal level of acceptance—a minimization of the Type I error.

What is sought is an easier statistic to compute but which essentially answers the same question as answered by the exact probability formula. The device: chi-square. The idea is remarkably simple and direct. Computation is easy. A cookbook recipe allows for immediate interpretation. But the statistical theory is complex. I shall allude only briefly to the theory. I shall pay considerable attention to computations. The algebra involved in effecting computational formulas must never be confused with deriving the chi-square argument.

Chi-square involves the following computations:

a. Determine the observed frequencies occurring in the cells of your table.

b. Determine the frequency you would expect to find if some particular theory is true. The sum of the frequencies in (a) must equal the sum of the frequencies in (b).

c. Take the difference between the observed and expected frequencies.

d. Square these differences. Among other things, negative signs are removed.

e. Divide these squared differences by their corresponding expected value.

f. Sum these terms.

The sum gives a statistic that has a chi-square distribution. All that need be known about this is that the probability of obtaining a chi-square as large or larger by chance alone can be determined. Indeed, for our purposes (since we are dealing only with the two-by-two table), we can get a chi-square as large as or larger than 3.841 five per cent of the time, and one as large as or larger than 6.635 one per cent of the time.

The formula for chi-square is, of course,

$$\chi^2 = \Sigma \frac{(O - E)^2}{E}$$

(4.22)

where the observed frequency is denoted by O, and the expected frequency by E. It has become common to use the marginal totals as given for the computation of E in 4.22, although this is not required by the formula.

	A	~A	t
C	a	b	$n_1.$
~C	c	d	$n_2.$
t	$n._1$	$n._2$	N

To determine the expected value associated with cell a, we determine the probability of the occurrence of an object in the row and column sharing this cell. In other words, we determine the probability of an object's being classified as A; then we determine the probability of its being classified as C. The former is found by dividing the column by N (i.e., obtaining $n._1/N$); the latter by dividing the row total by N (i.e., obtaining $n_1./N$). If the two probabilities are independent, the probability of the object's being both A and C (of being a) is the product of these probabilities. Hence the frequency expected on the assumption of independence is found by multiplying this expected probability by N.

$$E_a = N(n_1./N)(n._1/N) = (n_1.)(n._1)N$$

(4.23)

We could, of course, compute the expected values for each of the four cells, but this would entail useless labor. Since the marginal totals are fixed, the two-by-two table has only one degree of freedom—knowledge of one cell value completely implies the content of the rest. Since this is so, the magnitude of the difference between the observed and the expected frequencies is constant for all four cells. That this must be so is apparent: for what is taken from a must be added to both b and c in order to keep the marginals at the same value. What is added to c or b must be taken from d for the same reason. Clearly, 4.22 can be computed by determining the appropriate difference for any particular cell.

As a matter of fact, this ease of computation suggests that there must be a computational formula even easier than 4.22. I say "even easier" because 4.22 is a substitute for the clumsier 4.21. I shall show that this is so. The steps are not difficult.

4.22 requires the computation of four $(O-E)^2/E$ values. For the first cell, say, this would be

$$\frac{\left(a-\frac{n_1.n._1}{N}\right)^2}{\frac{n_1.n._1}{N}} \tag{4.24}$$

Using the appropriate modification of 4.23 and since the difference term is numerically the same for each required computation, 4.22 can be written in the following detailed way:

$$\chi^2=\frac{\left(a-\frac{n_1.n._1}{N}\right)^2}{\frac{n_1.n._1}{N}}+\frac{\left(a-\frac{n_1.n._1}{N}\right)^2}{\frac{n_1.n._2}{N}}+\frac{\left(a-\frac{n_1.n._1}{N}\right)^2}{\frac{n_2.n._1}{N}}+\frac{\left(a-\frac{n_1.n._1}{N}\right)^2}{\frac{n_2.n._2}{N}} \tag{4.25}$$

Because the numerator is constant for each cell, it may be taken out and put to the left of an operation requiring summing:

$$\chi^2=\left(a-\frac{n_1.n._1}{N}\right)^2\left(\frac{N}{n_1.n._1}+\frac{N}{n_1.n._2}+\frac{N}{n_2.n._1}+\frac{N}{n_2.n._2}\right) \tag{4.26}$$

Deriving the last term of the righthand member of 4.26, we have

$$\left[\frac{N}{n_1.n._1}+\frac{N}{n_1.n._2}+\frac{N}{n_2.n._1}+\frac{N}{n_2.n._2}\right]=N\left[\frac{1}{n_1.n._1}+\frac{1}{n_1.n._2}+\frac{1}{n_2.n._1}+\frac{1}{n_2.n._2}\right]$$

$$=N\left[\frac{1}{n_1.}\left(\frac{1}{n._1}+\frac{1}{n._2}\right)+\frac{1}{n_2.}\left(\frac{1}{n._1}+\frac{1}{n._2}\right)\right]$$

$$=N\left[\left(\frac{1}{n._1}+\frac{1}{n._2}\right)\left(\frac{1}{n_1.}+\frac{1}{n_2.}\right)\right]$$

$$= N\left[\left(\frac{n_{.2} + n_{.1}}{n_{.1}n_{.2}}\right)\left(\frac{n_{2.} + n_{1.}}{n_{1.}n_{2.}}\right)\right]$$

$$= N\left[\left(\frac{N}{n_{.1}n_{.2}}\right)\left(\frac{N}{n_{1.}n_{2.}}\right)\right]$$

$$= N^3\left[\frac{N}{n_{1.}n_{2.}n_{.1}n_{.2}}\right]$$

(4.27)

Deriving, now, the first term of (4.26), we obtain

$$\left(a - \frac{n_{1.}n_{.1}}{N}\right)^2 = \left(\frac{aN - n_{1.}n_{.1}}{N}\right)^2$$

$$= \frac{(aN - n_{1.}n_{.1})^2}{N^2}$$

Recalling that N equals the sum of the cell values, that $n_{1.} = a + b$ and $n_{.1} = a + c$,

$$= \frac{[a(a + b + c + d) - (a + b)(a + c)]}{N^2}$$

$$= \frac{[(a^2 + ab + ac + ad) - (a^2 + ab + ac + bc)]^2}{N^2}$$

$$= (a^2 + ab + ac + ad - a^2 - ab - ac - bc)^2$$

$$= \frac{(ad - bc)^2}{N^2}$$

(4.28)

To get a computational form for chi-square, we must combine 4.27 with 4.28. This gives

$$\chi^2 = \frac{(ad - bc)^2 N^3}{N^2} \frac{1}{n_{.1}n_{.2}n_{1.}n_{2.}} = \frac{(ad - bc)^2 N}{n_{.1}n_{.2}n_{1.}n_{2.}}$$

(4.29)

which is readily recognized as the standard shortcut formula for computing chi-square from a two-by-two table. All that I have done is to show that 4.29 gives precisely the same result as 4.22. Hence, any interpretation of 4.22 is appropriate to 4.29. In general, I should say that 4.22 gives my specification of chi-square, but 4.29 gives a computational technique.

Now, chi-square is seen to measure the difference between an observed set of frequencies and those expected if the two probability systems were independent. For that reason, this form of chi-square is often referred to as a test of independence. If we accept the .05 level as the critical point, any chi-square greater than 3.841 will enable us to reject chance as an explanation. If chi-square is less than 3.841, we would say that chance is sufficient to explain our distribution, although it is not a *necessary* explanation. We may wrongfully reject chance.

An extended example. Consider the following illustration. The universe to be studied is teachers. These will be the subjects of any proposition we seek to establish. Now teachers will be more or less successful: "successful" and "unsuccessful" will be the predicate terms in one proposition. Teachers' training varies; the predicate term will be "teachers' college" and "college or university." It is especially important to note that one samples members of the subject category. In the following example, therefore, one will not be permitted to draw inferences regarding the relation of the various predicate terms for "other than teachers." Of course, if one has a theoretical reason for believing that "teachers" is like other possible categories, one has reason to assert generalizations beyond the confines of the immediate data. When this is done, it should be recalled, considerable risk is entailed.

Unless one subscribes to a strong causal monism, one is never able to contradict the point of the preceding paragraph. In the most extreme case imaginable to a social scientist, one may have a subject term comprised of "man"—as in the proposition "All men are mortal." In order for one to discuss such a category in a way that would relate the predicate terms to "other than man," the research system would have to be tremendously complicated. For most purposes, one may reject considerations of "other than man" simply because they are irrelevant to the argument. The relation between kind of college training and success for, say, horses is simply not interesting to most sociologists. But even if some category "not man" were introduced, all would, presumably, belong to some other more general term whose contradiction would not be studied. Clearly, this can drag us down the trail of metascience, and further away from the task of a given science.

It is entirely possible that the subtle role of the subject term has confounded the thinking of many erstwhile statisticians who long for a complete overthrow of categorical logic. Even in the simplest kind of research, however, elementary issues must be considered. Nor can it be assumed that adults naturally develop a correct logic, that, owing to some happy circumstance of this world, a rigorous logic is forced on the observer. This harks back to the passive notion of research where the world shot forth stimuli whose purpose was to stimulate the sense organs of waiting scientists. Unfortunately, various forms of logical argument have shown historical development well beyond the sense experience of any one observer. Unless one subscribes to a doctrine of ontogeny recapitulating phylogeny, this is a tenuous position to hold. Unhappily, however, it seems to be a fact that many colleges and universities have found it necessary to teach logic. And, worse, students have been known to fail exams in logic, even after they have been taught correct logic. If that were not bad enough, adult scientists have been known to reason incorrectly and to arrive at invalid conclusions. The world need not be logical; but researchers need logic to insure correct inferences.

The immediate question, of course, is Is the probability of having teachers' college training independent of the probability of success? There are, presumably, two empirical answers to this question: given a specifically designated subuniverse (say, teachers in Minneapolis, Minnesota), what is the relation between the two probabilities? This is related to the historical empiricism discussed earlier. But if one is not particularly interested in the relation of the probabilities as it occurs in Minneapolis, one may create subuniverses of teachers' college graduates and college or university graduates and sample equally between them. Ordinarily, the latter is more difficult to do, although more related to the logic of the experiment, since it appeals as much to "process" as it does to history.

Consider the following hypothetical situation. One hundred teachers who graduated from a teachers' college and one hundred who had graduated from a liberal arts college or the state university could be sampled. Assuming that success is independently defined, something like the following table would not be impossible.

	Teachers' College	College or University	Total
Successful	59	48	107
Unsuccessful	41	52	93
Total	100	100	200

We get the following results:

$a = 59$	$b = 48$	$N = 200$
$c = 41$	$d = 52$	$n_1. = 107$
$n_{.1} = 100$	$n_{.2} = 100$	$n_2. = 93$

Inserting these in 4.29, we get

$$\chi^2 = \frac{[(59)(52) - (48)(41)]^2 \, 200}{(100)(100)(107)(93)} = 2.37$$

$$(4.30)$$

This is much smaller than the required 3.841; hence we are unable to reject chance. This implies that, as far as we know, it does not make any real difference whether a teacher was trained in a teachers' college or at a college or university as far as success is concerned. It is true that the number of successes was greater for the teachers' college group, but this was a statistical mirage. The existing distribution is within the range of what would be deduced if we have appealed only to the laws of probability. Since the laws of probability are sufficient to explain our observation, no further appeal is sensible, unless one wishes to control some factor (to further restrict the subject term of the fundamental proposition).

A correction for continuity. The chi-square test is, we remember, only a substitute for a more rigorous technique. Imagine the difficulty of employing the exact probability method in the table above. In developing a reasonable substitute, some assumptions had to be made.

In particular, the expected frequency involved in the computation is subject to some restrictions. Consider, for example, the state of affairs if, for some cell, the expected frequency were to approach zero—to be, in fact, much less than unity. Dividing by a number approaching zero results in a number approaching infinity. Obviously, this sort of thing makes interpretation difficult. But more than that, it would contradict the assumptions of the chi-square analysis.

As a matter of fact, the expected frequency must be rather large. No one knows just what that means. George Snedecor thinks that the expected frequency for any cell ought to be 200 or more.[12] Fisher and Yates thinks that some correction must be made when the expected frequency is less than 500.[13] Some statisticians try to make a habit of always computing chi-square with a correction. These restrictions apply particularly to the case where the chi-square has but one degree of freedom.[14]

Since the correction always reduces the magnitude of chi-square, it is of particular importance in those cases where the significance level is barely reached. In such an instance, the correction may lead to a different conclusion.

Some statisticians claim that the significant limit is that the expected frequency should never be smaller than 5 and then χ^2 ought not be used, let alone corrected. They point out that 4.22 may be rewritten in the following way:

$$\chi^2 = N\Sigma \frac{(P_0 - P_E)^2}{P_E} \qquad (4.31)$$

Instead of frequencies in the computation, 4.31 requires the use of observed and expected probabilities. Now, the distribution of chi-square in no way depends upon the source of the expected probabilities. As a matter of fact, any arbitrary choice, as long as the sum of the expected probabilities equals unity, will work. This being so, one wonders whether or not the stringent requirement is significant. There is no real rule within the logic of probability theory that answers the question of how big the smallest expected frequency should be. Those who vaunt conservatism usually choose a rather large number. There is no proof that the expected frequency must be larger than any arbitrary choice.

In any event, it is probably wise to note the form which the correction takes. Essentially, it simply means the subtraction of a half-unit from the difference between the observed and expected frequencies. Accordingly, 4.22 would be written

$$\chi^2 = \Sigma \frac{(\mid O - E \mid - \frac{1}{2})^2}{E} \qquad (4.32)$$

and 4.29 would be written

$$\chi^2 = \frac{\left(\mid ad - bc \mid - \frac{N}{2}\right)^2 N}{n_{.1}n_{.2}n_1.n_2.} \qquad (4.33)$$

It really isn't too bad and is not important, except in doubtful cases; and then 4.33 may make you change your mind.

CHAPTER 5

Alternatives to Chance

BEFORE one can develop an argument—that is, before one can build a set of propositions into a theory—one must ascertain how they are related. Some propositions are related through the device of definitions. Others may or may not be related, depending upon fact. It should be clear by now that two-termed propositions for which operational specifications exist can be tested for independence. The means considered so far are the exact probability and the chi-square tests.

Practically no research is conducted in the social sciences but what a test is made of the null hypothesis. After a review of the literature, the modern scientific writer blandly says, "and so we tested the hypothesis of no difference."[1] Worse, perhaps, are those who will carefully indicate that they really believe two groups are interestingly different. Then they tell us, "so we will test the null hypothesis that there is no difference."

The major objection to this formulation is the confusion it brings to the idea of a hypothesis. A minor objection is that it tends to prevent the researcher from considering the null hypothesis as a real alternative. That the researcher does not believe the null hypothesis is generally obvious from the way papers are written. Yet few contemporary writers suggest that there could be more than one alternative to the null hypothesis. As we shall see in another connection, there are many alternatives to the null hypothesis in the case of the two-by-two table.

The major objection to the traditional statement of the null hypothesis is that it is not a hypothesis at all. A proposition is made: these groups differ in some respect. A statement which is equivalent to "I doubt that these differ in the respect named" is offered as a "null hypothesis." That is, the form used by most contemporary writers has the null hypothesis as a statement doubting the particular alternative they have in mind. Now, a proposition is not a hypothesis (although a hypothesis is a proposition). Neither is a proposition which is doubted although one doubts a hypothesis—and therefore tests it. One can and does doubt a great many propositions, none of which is considered a hypothesis.

Thus, it happens that I doubt that the moon is made of cheese, green or otherwise. A formal statement of doubt does not elevate the assertion to the status of a hypothesis. I am certain that the reader can call to mind a lot of things which he doubts. I doubt that it will rain tomorrow. I doubt that I shall see a unicorn in the garden. The fact that I doubt these things cannot be sensibly disputed. This is not the locus of the criticism. The major point is that a hypothesis is a particular kind of proposition. In the first place, it is a tentative solution to some problem. Few researchers consider exactly how the so-called null hypothesis can solve their problem. Generally, it cannot solve their problem. It is not a serious contender. In the second place, a hypothesis, properly considered, is a statement of relations. What is generally given is a corruption of a premise in some sensible hypothesis. If the hypothesis does not contain some semblance of a mathematically defined functional relation, at least the propositional form "If P, then Q" is invoked in a hypothesis. Traditionally, this is the *form* of the hypothesis. Perhaps social scientists have been so busily trained in computational procedure that they have been forced to neglect a traditional training in logic.

The null hypothesis contains an appeal to probability theory. It begins with the assumption that the laws of probability alone are sufficient to explain a given observation. Then a particular statistic is noted—a chi-square, a critical ratio, a correlation coefficient, or what have you—and, for the level of confidence specified, an inference of the magnitude of the statistic is made. Accordingly, one would present an argument of this form (let us use our chi-square with one degree of freedom and the .05 level of significance for our example):

MAJOR PREMISE: If the laws of probability, assuming independence, are sufficient to explain my observed frequencies, then chi-square will be less than 3.841.

MINOR PREMISE (from research): Chi-square is of such-and-such a size.

CONCLUSION: (a) If the chi-square were greater than 3.841 the conclusion reached would be false, and hence the null hypothesis would be false. (b) If the chi-square were less than 3.841 no conclusion could be reached; but the null hypothesis—the major premise—could not be rejected as it is still a sufficient explanation.

It is probably true that reading such a formalistic statement of the null hypothesis would be boring, especially if the argument were appealed to several times during the study. Quite properly, some shorthand statement must be available. Unfortunately, the contemporary use of the null hypothesis does not allow the inference that the user has a proper regard for what a hypothesis is. As a matter of fact, one can generally doubt the ability of most researchers to estimate the significance of a proposition.

Since few researchers formally consider the implications of the null hypothesis, few seem to consider the null hypothesis as a real contender for a body of science. At the same time, there are a few notable cases of sociological significance in which null hypothesis could be *accepted* and given theoretical status.[2] Consider, for example, the problem of the automobile accident. If accidental means "outside a given causal system," then certain accidents must occur independently of, say, a sociological causal system. It may turn out, that is to say, that "social class" and "ethnic background" are independent of accidents. With respect to a given sociological dimension, the data may be independent.

Another situation is found in demography. How does one *sociologically* or *psychologically* explain sex of child at birth? We may well assume that there are both sociological and psychological implications of the sex of a child at birth. Sex may well be an antecedent condition to subsequent behavior, and in that situation, a rejection of the null hypothesis would likely occur. But consider sex of child at birth as a consequent: one is likely to have to appeal to chance, unless some biological factor like diet connected to social class is involved.

Research directors, particularly, find themselves in an ambivalent situation regarding the null hypothesis. Many, to be sure, are infatuated with the semblance of rigor its use gives, and dearly love to see proposals abound in statements of doubt. It may be that foundations, when acting upon research requests, are also entranced with this particular vehicle. This would make sense if the proposal contained the modern notation

H:0 for the null hypothesis: this makes it scientific, which is as impressive to the untrained as the Greek alphabet is to the unlettered.

But because of the possibility of there being a number of alternatives to the null hypothesis, a proposal containing only the null form must be considered elliptical. If only two alternatives exist, one may perhaps work out an argument showing how the substantive hypothesis contradicts that of the null form. But if more than two alternatives exist, contradiction is impossible. The importance of noting whether the substantive hypothesis is contrary or contradictory must be known to the reader.[3] Briefly, the importance is this: if the null and the substantive hypotheses are contradictory, then one may arrive at a conclusion by falsifying or verifying either. The null hypothesis is clearly the one to work on.

If the two competing hypotheses are contrary to each other, then the falsification of the one does not require the inference of the other. It may well be that both can be false—especially if another alternative is known to be possible. In this instance, the falsification of a weak hypothesis of "no difference" does not aid in the demonstration of that which was really sought. Generally, if more attention is paid to the formal statement of the null hypothesis, a way out of this apparent impasse can be found. Fortunately, few substantive hypotheses are important enough to make much of a fuss over.

I have briefly mentioned the hypothesis concerning independent probabilities. I have alluded to another common hypothesis. When one has samples of two sets of conditions, a sensible question is "are these two conditions different in respect to some interesting outcome?" The type of outcome we are particularly interested in is the proportion of each sample being a success. We may observe the number of times one achieves the consequent under conditions A, and also observe the number of times it is achieved under $\sim$A. We may ask the common question, is the difference between the two proportions *really* zero? Obviously, we are talking about a null hypothesis.

Although our substantive argument may suggest that one particular proportion ought to be higher than the other (as an extreme, one ought to approach unity, the other approach zero), our null hypothesis is supposed to require a *difference* in the neighborhood of zero. Actually, the null hypothesis would be structurally similar to the previous one:

MAJOR PREMISE: If the differences between my sample proportions are in the neighborhood of zero (if the laws of probability are sufficient to explain the differences between my sample proportions), then a statistic called "critical ratio" will be less than 1.96.[4]

MINOR PREMISE: My observed critical ratio is of such-and-such a size.

CONCLUSION: As before: if the statistic is greater than that specified in the minor premise, the assumption of chance is in error; if the statistic is smaller than that specified, chance is a sufficient explanation of the observed difference.

In the next section, I shall show that one particular critical ratio of proportions is intimately related to chi-square for the two-by-two table.

The relation between critical ratio and chi-square. The critical ratio of difference between two proportions, with variance determined from a weighted average proportion, when squared is equal to chi-square for a two-by-two table. We may symbolize critical ratio in the following manner (some may prefer to call this a t test, some may call it Z—and perhaps it is known by other names):

$$CR = \frac{p_1 - p_2}{\sqrt{PQ\left(\dfrac{1}{n_{.1}} + \dfrac{1}{n_{.2}}\right)}} \tag{5.1}$$

Now let the following denotations and relations be accepted:

a = the number of successes in sample A
c = the number of failures in sample A
$n_{.1} = a + c$
b = the number of successes in sample $\sim A$
d = the number of failures in sample $\sim A$
$n_{.2} = b + d$
$N = n_{.1}\, n_{.2}$
$n_{1.} = a + b$
$n_{2.} = c + d$

These may be expressed in our two-by-two table:

	Sample A	Sample $\sim A$	Total
Successes	a	b	$n_1.$
Failures	c	d	$n_2.$
Total	$n_{.1}$	$n_{.2}$	N

Now we will let

$$p_1 = \frac{a}{n._1}$$

$$p_2 = \frac{b}{n._2}$$

$$P = \frac{n._1 p_1 + n._2 p_2}{n._1 + n._2} = \frac{a+b}{N} = \frac{n_1.}{N} \qquad (5.4)$$

Clearly,

$$Q = 1 - P = \frac{n_1.}{N} = \frac{N - n_1.}{N} = \frac{n_2.}{N} \qquad (5.5)$$

Squaring 5.1 gives us

$$CR^2 = \frac{(p_1 - p_2)^2}{PQ\dfrac{1}{n._1} + \dfrac{1}{n._2}} \qquad (5.6)$$

Rationalizing the parenthetic term in the denominator we get

$$\frac{1}{n._1} + \frac{1}{n._2} = \frac{n._2 + n_1.}{n._1 n._2} = \frac{N}{n._1 n._2}$$

Substituting this along with 5.2, 5.3, 5.4, and 5.5 in 5.6, we get

$$CR = \frac{\left(\dfrac{a}{n._1} - \dfrac{b}{n._2}\right)^2}{\dfrac{n_1.}{N}\dfrac{n_2.}{N}\left(\dfrac{N}{n._1 n._2}\right)}$$

$$= \frac{\left(\dfrac{n._2 a - n._1 b}{n._1 n._2}\right)^2}{\dfrac{n_1. n_2.}{N(n._1 n._2)}}$$

$$= \frac{[(b+d)a - (a+c)b]^2}{(n._1 n._2)^2} \cdot \frac{N(n._1 n._2)}{n_1. n_2.}$$

$$= \frac{(ab + ad - ab - bc)^2 N}{(n._1 n._2)(n_1. n_2.)}$$

$$= \frac{(ad - bc)^2 N}{n._1 n._2 n_1. n_2.}$$

$$= \chi^2$$

which is the desired result, as this equals 4.29 of the preceding chapter.

Alternatives to chance. Unless the chance explanation contradicts the substantive proposition offered, there are usually many alternatives to chance. If the relationship is significant—that is, if chance is rejected, we can see at least six conditions which would likely sustain a rejection of chance.

Case I. If-and-only-if (strong)

	A	~A
C	C	0
~C	0	

Case II. Implication (weak)

	A	~A
C	C	
~C	0	

Case III. Subimplication (weak)

	A	~A
C	C	0
~C	~C	

Case IV. Contrariety (weak)

	A	~A
C	0	
~C	~C	

Case V. Subcontrariety (weak)

	A	~A
C	C	
~C	~C	0

ALTERNATIVES TO CHANCE
Case VI. Contradiction (strong)

$$A \qquad \sim A$$

$$C$$

$$\sim C \qquad \qquad 0$$

Which of these alternatives is required by the theory involved in the research? In this discussion A and C are given meaning such that this sequence is theoretically important. That is, the antecedent is distinguished from the consequent in terms of substantive theory, not by arbitrary choice.

These forms are familiar. We encountered them in Chapter 2 during a discussion of logical relations.

Since we are making substantive propositions about an existential world, the condition of 0 ought to be modified to $\rightarrow 0$ (approaches zero). This is consistent with our principle of errorful operational specifications. Clearly, probabilistic statements will result from any test of relations between A and C for "All S," where S denotes the universe from which the sample was drawn. Good research contains explicit reference to the universe members as subject terms of fundamental propositions. In most cases the reference is implicit at best.

Sometimes, it would seem, the researcher has no notion of what alternative he is to expect. Then, perhaps, he may be content to find any alternative to chance: but he would not have proved any particular relation. Sometimes he may discover that a particular relation has occurred in other researches. He may predict that such a relation will exist in his data—and find it so. But this does not make the relation theoretically important. Unless the terms of the propositions have such a relation to theory that a given relation is theoretically expected, no proof is contained in a rejection of chance.

However, if one's theory is so rigorous as to permit an inference of a particular kind of relation, then a demonstration of a rejection of chance, provided that the relation appears as fact, may be taken as a verification of the theory. That theories are never proved is a function of our logical system, which is strongest in instances of negation. But a test which is unable to falsify a theory is taken as its verification.

What I am suggesting is that logical relations may be considered as models for research. By now, we are accustomed to mathematical models in the social sciences. Considerable debate has gone on over what they are and are not, but there seems to be consensus on the following points: a model is formal (that is, a form of a relation is specified); the terms of the model exist in terms already contained in the theory; the particular form is *required*—in the sense of logical necessity—by the theory. The model is then subjected to test. Failure to reject the model is taken as a verification of it.

An example from contemporary research. Consider the behavior of members of a bureaucracy.[5] A traditional argument of sociology is that personality is a function of culture. An older argument had been that culture is a function of personality (human nature). It took some doing for sociologists to establish their point of view. One implication of their doctrine is immediately apparent: people become like the social system in which they live and interact with each other.

If it is true that people apprehend their social world, it should be possible for a researcher to measure that apprehension. Let us assume that if a person is offered a representation of his world, he will affirm it only if it corresponds to his image of that world. Further, if it is possible for people to evaluate their world, it should be possible for a researcher to obtain a measure of that evaluation. Assume that if a person is offered a proposition describing how people *ought* to behave, he will subscribe to it if it corresponds to his moral evaluation of his world. In short, it is possible for a sociologist to measure both a subject's conception of what the world is like and what the world ought to be like.

The initial question is What is the relation between the subject's impressions of how the world is and his impressions of how it ought to be? It is possible, of course, that there is no relation, and that the two sets of impressions are independent. If attitudes and beliefs were epiphenomenal, a state of independence would exist (though independence may exist under conditions other than this). At any rate, the answer to the question will involve a test of independence.

Besides the issue of independence, there is the question What form will the relationship between beliefs about what is the case and beliefs about what ought to be the case take? If the sociologist's traditional belief that personality is shaped by culture is true, it would further seem reasonable to infer that a judgment of what is must be logically prior to a judgment of what ought to be. That is, one's belief about what is *implies* a belief in what ought to be. In tabular form:

	Is	
	Belief accepted	*Belief rejected*
Ought:		
Belief accepted		
Belief rejected	→0	

A contrary theoretical argument can be developed. In it, one would proceed from ideas about perception. It would freely admit that personality is learned, and so, for that matter, are beliefs about what ought to be. That is not the point. The point is that if one has certain moral beliefs and he has an emotional stake in a situation, he will build his observations according to his moral code. This implies that beliefs about what ought to be must be logically prior to beliefs about what is. Rather than requiring that beliefs about what is imply beliefs about what ought to be, one could require that a belief about what is be implied by a belief about what ought to be.

Here we have a fairly common state of affairs. We can develop three contrary arguments regarding beliefs about what is and what ought to be. (a) The two belief systems are independent. (b) "Is" and "ought" are connected by a relation of implication. (c) "Is" and "ought" are connected by a relation of subimplication. Which is correct? There are several ways out. One can address himself simply to the facts, i.e., to the data contained in the questionnaire, and choose whatever results. Clearly, this is no proof. It begs the question of how to choose among the alternatives to chance.

What one must do is to note the characteristics of the research situation. The statements are not completely general, but are restricted to special conditions. What are some of these conditions? The major one is that the research concerned a bureaucracy in a southern American city. An alternative to "People become like the system" is "Certain systems select the kind of people who work in them." If the latter is true, one may suspect that employees in a particular bureaucracy are not a random sample of the adult United States population, but a restricted subgroup. If this is so, it is likely that a consciousness of likeness exists: members of the office staff probably feel an identity with each other. This implies that they have some ego involvement with the organization, which in turn suggests a commitment of the sort required for the argument that people build their perceptions of their social world according to their commitment to it. Accordingly, we choose the third alternative.

Observe that we may be shown wrong in two ways: if the null hypothesis is not falsified or if some other alternative exists, in particular if the relation is that of implication. The following table gives the data obtained in a recent study. The beliefs concerned the use of rules to govern agency office behavior. A (Like a bureaucracy) denotes beliefs consistent with a frame of reference and $\sim A$ (Not like a bureaucracy) beliefs contrary to that frame of reference. If bureaucrats become like the system, then beliefs that their world was a bureaucratic one ought to be prior to a belief that they ought to be governed like bureaucrats.

	Is		
Ought:	*Like a bureaucracy*	*Not like a bureaucracy*	*Total*
Like a bureaucracy	37	2	39
Not like a bureaucracy	24	33	57
Total	61	35	96

It is quite evident that 3.3 is most similar to the results obtained. It is equally clear that these findings are consistent with the relation of subimplication. We can take it that the substantive hypothesis has been verified; chi-square equals 27.83 and is obviously beyond a chance explanation.

Among other things, it must be most carefully noted that we have neither a theoretical nor a statistical reason to hope for zeros in the minor diagonal. Although this notion was proposed as a modification of Znaniecki's analytical induction, it is clearly without merit. It apparently was based upon a formal notion of research rather than on a theoretical acceptance of logical form as research models.

The implications of this discussion for research design are far-reaching. Not only must one discern substantive alternatives, but one must observe their relations in order that a design may properly allow a choice. The null hypothesis can be considered a serious contender, if properly developed; hence its relation to other alternatives must be noted. Recall, in particular, that the null hypothesis is consistent with a relation of independence. Various alternatives may take various logical forms. Which of these, if any, is *required* by theory is not a technical question. If a scientist is afraid of thinking lest it prove to be too subjective, if he would prefer to use a "cookbook," then he need not worry about making the choices suggested here. But if the scientist is willing to drop the role of passive technician, if he is willing to be active, to take on a creative role, then he will immediately address himself to theory to determine what structure his argument is to take. What I have said in regard to logical models applies equally to mathematical models. The only distinction one need note here is that one must develop that model which best fits the postulates of his operational specifications. If one cannot properly assert degrees of quantity, the development of logical models seems all the more imperative. Various sociologists have asserted that science seeks to make "If A, then B" statements. Herein is provided an argument elevating this form from a desideratum to a potential model to guide research. Rigor need not be made equivalent to quantification. And in no circumstance can mere technical competence replace the ability to think.

Degrees of approximation. We have seen that logical relation between propositions can be graphically represented by the two-by-two table. We noted, moreover, that necessary, sufficient, and necessary and sufficient conditions were particular logical relations. We further commented on how causality can be subsumed under the rubric "type of relation." A point to recall is that a certain amount of knowledge about the terms encompassed in the relationship is not revealed in the form itself. In other words, the two-by-two table gives a *formal* structure; other content may be appealed to. The formal consideration is no small matter. Two immediate problems exist. The first, of course, is establishing the possible existence of a given logical relation. This is done by testing for independence. The second problem relates to the use of the two-by-two table as a logical model. If there is theoretical reason to expect a given form, its eventuation in fact may be taken as a verification of the hypothecated form. *This section suggests ways of measuring the degree to which the logical model is in fact approximated by the data at hand.*

The approach is simple and direct. The first operation tests the proposition that none of the usually considered logical relations exists, i.e., that the propositions are statistically independent. In the case of independence, probability theory is an adequate solution. As one departs from independence toward any of the other logical relations, premises additional to probability must be adduced.

As we have seen, the simplest test of independence is the chi-square test. We have seen also that, for the two-by-two table, the shortcut formula is permissible. Accordingly, we have

$$\chi^2 = \frac{(ad - bc)^2 N}{n_{.1} n_{.2}}$$

(5.8)

whose terms are given in the following table:

	A	~A	t
C	a	b	$n_1.$
~C	c	d	$n_2.$
t	$n_{.1}$	$n_{.2}$	N

Clearly, chi-square has a limiting value in the event that any cell approaches zero—in the event, that is, that one of the logical relations alternative to independence exists. Hence, a reasonable measure of the approximation of the empirical distribution to a logical model involves a ratio of an empirically determined chi-square to its maximum value under conditions required by the logical model. This ratio will be denoted as ϕ^2 (phi-square), and $0 \leq \phi^2 \leq 1$.

Case I. If-and-only-if (strong). Because the if-and-only-if (or necessary and sufficient conditions) is popularly regarded as an ideal state of affairs, I shall consider that ratio first. It is represented by Case I on page 92.

	A	~A	t
C	a	0	$n_1.$
~C	0	d	$n_2.$
t	$n_{.1}$	$n_{.2}$	N

Obviously, $a = n_1.$ and $d = n_2. = n_{.2}$. If we insert the appropriate values in 5.8 we get

$$\chi^2 = \frac{(ad - 0)^2 N}{n_1. n_2. n_{.1} n_{.2}} = \frac{ad^2 N}{(ad)(ad)} = N$$

(5.9)

Consequently, for this model, phi-square would be defined as

$$\phi^2_1 = \frac{\chi^2}{N} \qquad (5.10)$$

This result is no surprise. Indeed, this is a rather old measure. It has, however, gone under some other names. Sometimes it has been called fourfold r; in this situation it has been called "analogous to r^2." Exactly what the limits on the analogy were, no one seems to have known or cared. Another designation was mean-square contingency. This is easily seen from a purely technical point of view. If chi-square really measures squared contingency, and if N is sample size, then squared contingency divided by the size of the sample is a "mean squared contingency." What inferences follow upon this knowledge is, of course, obscure. No one really knew or cared. Actually, this is a dubious interpretation; no theoretical meaning could be directly apprehended. But the knowledge that N, instead of being sample size, is the maximum value of chi-square (a fact long known) should generate a rather sensible interpretation—namely, the one we offer here: the ratio of an empirically computed chi-square to its maximum.

That this interpretation was never suggested earlier is the result of a simple fact of life. N is not always the maximum value for chi-square, even for the two-by-two table. What was not noted was that the maximum value varied according to the particular model being considered. Thus, we entertain Case II.

Case II. Implication (weak). The next case to consider proposes the "If A, then C" relation. This is shown in Case II, page 92.

	A	$\sim$A	t
C	a	b	$n_1.$
$\sim$C	0	d	$n_2.$
t	$n._1$	$n._2$	N

Here we observe that $a = n._1$ and $d = n_2.$; plugging these values into 5.8 we get for the maximum value of chi-square the following:

$$\chi^2 = \frac{(ad - 0)^2 N}{n._1 n._2 n_1. n_2.}$$

99

But

$$\text{ad} = (n_{.1})(n_{2.}) = \frac{(n_{.1}n_{2.})^2 N}{n_{.1}n_{.2}n_{1.}n_{2.}} = \frac{n_{.1}n_{2.}}{n_{1.}n_{.2}} N$$

(5.11)

Thus, phi-square would be given by the following:

$$\phi^2{}_{II} = \frac{\dfrac{(\text{ad} - \text{bc})^2 N}{n_1.n_2.n_{.1}n_{.2}}}{\dfrac{n_{.1}n_{2.}N}{n_1.n_{.2}}}$$

$$= \frac{(\text{ad} - \text{bc})^2 N}{n_1.n_2.n_{.1}n_{.2}} \cdot \frac{n_1.n_{.2}}{n_{.1}n_{2.}N}$$

$$= \frac{(\text{ad} - \text{bc})^2}{(n_{.1}n_{2.})^2}$$

$$= \left(\frac{\text{ad} - \text{bc}}{n_{.1}n_{2.}}\right)$$

(5.12)

Then the square root of phi would be

$$\phi_{II} = \frac{\text{ad} - \text{bc}}{n_{.1}n_{.2}}$$

(5.13)

No new knowledge is gained by this operation except, perhaps, direction, if ad is less than bc; but it is simpler to compute—and there are those who are fascinated by the fact that the square root of a decimal is larger than the decimal itself.

The remaining four cases involve nothing new by way of a derivation. The steps are identical with the foregoing. However, as a summary, I shall show the tabular representation and the name, the maximum value which chi-square can achieve under this limitation, and the formula for obtaining phi-square.

Case III. Subimplication (weak)

	A	~A	t	Maximum value of chi-square
C	a	0	$n_1.$	
				$\chi^2 = \dfrac{n_1.n_{.2}}{n_{.1}n_2.} N$
~C	c	d	$n_2.$	
				Phi-square
t	$n_{.1}$	$n_{.2}$	N	$\phi^2{}_{III} = \left(\dfrac{\text{ad} - \text{bc}}{n_1.n_{.2}}\right)^2$ (5.14)

Case IV. Contrariety (weak)

	A	~A	t	Maximum value of chi-square
C	0	b	$n_1.$	
~C	c	d	$n_2.$	
t	$n._1$	$n._2$	N	

$$\chi^2 = \frac{n_1.n._1}{n_2.n._2} N$$

Phi-square

$$\phi^2{}_{IV} = \frac{ad - bc}{n_1.n._1}{}^2 \qquad (5.15)$$

Case V. Subcontrariety (weak)

	A	~A	t	Maximum value of chi-square
C	a	b	$n_1.$	
~C	c	0	$n_2.$	
t	$n._1$	$n._2$	N	

$$\chi^2 = \frac{n._2 n_2.}{n._1 n_1.}$$

Phi-square

$$\frac{ad - bc}{n_2.n._2} \qquad (5.16)$$

Case VI. Contradiction (strong)

	A	~A	t	Maximum value of chi-square
C	0	b	$n_1.$	
~C	c	0	$n_2.$	
t	$n._1$	$n._2$	N	

$$\chi^2 = N$$

Phi-square

$$\phi^2{}_{VI} = \frac{\chi^2}{N}$$

$$(5.17)$$

With these tables, some games can be played. Suppose that certain marginal totals are fixed such that particular ratios are possible. Thus, in Case V (for a sufficient example), if $n_1. = n._1$, then the maximum value for chi-square would be

$$\left(\frac{n_2.}{n_1.} \right)^2 N$$

If, then, $n_1. = n_2.$, the relation of subcontrariety would give way to that of contradiction.

The importance of this is far-reaching for design. It should be recalled that the numerical value of the difference between the observed and the expected value for any cell is constant for the entire table. This means that if the marginal totals of one dimension equal the marginals of the other, any displacement from chance will force the if-and-only-if model. In particular, if the researcher obtains the dichotomies by cutting a pair of quantities at the median, the only possible model is that of the if-and-only-if relation. It is entirely possible to develop a theory connecting, say, mechanization with farm fatalities in such a way that the expected relation is that of implication. If the unit of analysis is measured on both dimensions and dichotomies obtained by cutting at the median, one cannot test for the weak relation of implication. For this reason, one must approach dichotomization of quantitatively defined measures with care. Too often, it would seem, the researcher is oblivious to the notion that the two-by-two table evokes an image of a logical relation. Hence, theoretically sterile cutting points are often used simply because they are traditional. Ordinarily, the following rule of thumb may prove helpful: if one has reason to suspect that the quantitative measures are theoretically linearly related, dichotomies at the median are appropriate; however, if one suspects a curvilinear relation, the median is an inappropriate cutting point since the model will force an assumption of linearity.

The converse also holds. If the margins are not equal, the if-and-only-if relation cannot appear. It seems clear that one must determine the magnitude of the marginals with considerable care. Prudence would suggest that the numbers of members in the A and $\sim$A samples can be controlled at will: these may be equal with no implication as to the magnitude of the other marginals, and, hence, no implication to the form per se. Extreme care must be exercised in limiting the number of members of the terms defining the consequent. It is here that one may jeopardize his theoretical work.

After all, it would be futile to develop a theoretical requirement for a particular form (to use a logical relation as a research model) and then contradict that requirement by a thoughtless research operation. At the same time, one ought not be a discoverer of the assumptions built into his research operations: to have implicitly required a strong relation by virtue of having controlled the marginals ought not make one be too surprised at inferring it from the data should chance be rejected.

A brief recapitulation: Logical relations can sensibly be proposed as theoretical models for research. These relations exist as alternatives to chance. Not only can a chi-square of a two-by-two table permit an evaluation of the sufficiency of chance as an explanation, it also provides sufficient information to enable one to measure the degree to which an empirically defined chi-square approached its empiricial maximum. For the example on p. 100, we can see that the appropriate case is III—subimplication. Chi-square was 27.83. The other necessary data are

$$n_{.1} = 61$$

$$n_{2.} = 57$$

$$n_{1.} = 39$$

$$n_{.2} = 35$$

$$N = 96$$

Inserting these in the formula for maximum chi-square we get

$$\chi^2_{max} = \frac{(39)(35)(96)}{(61)(57)} \cong 38$$

$$(5.13)$$

Then,

$$\phi^2_{III} = \frac{27.8}{38} = .73$$

$$(5.14)$$

This says we obtained 73 per cent of the chi-square implied by our model. Had we used mean-square contingency, we would have obtained

$$\phi^2 = \frac{27.8}{96} = .29$$

$$(5.15)$$

The difference is sizable. To use the latter because it is conservative does not seem to merit much attention. Just why fitting an improper model is either conservative or praiseworthy seems obscure.

CHAPTER 6

Other Measures of Association

As ONE would surmise, a nonsignificant chi-square permits the assertion of no association (whatever association may mean). Thus, if a chi-square were in the neighborhood of zero, phi-square would also be. Hence, before making any measure of association, one must test for independence. It is grappling with ghosts to measure something that isn't there.

The idea behind phi-square is not spectacular. It must be one of those measures that occur to a great many people. Some of the measures considered in this chapter may also seem unspectacular. Others will not.

I shall pursue no derivations in this chapter. When I use any mathematics beyond computational formulae it will be merely to acquaint readers further with the statistic in question. Certain peculiarities and limits of equations can easily be ascertained by plugging in known limits (usually 0's, sometimes 1's) in appropriate places and watching what results. When I do this, the reader may be certain that the mathematics will be simple. In particular, I shall discuss the following statistics: (a) Yule's Q, (b) the coefficient of contingency, (c) tetrachoric correlation—r_t, lambda—a predictive measure, and Jahn's index of segregation.

Yule's Q. For the tabular representation we have maintained,

	A	~A
C	a	b
~C	c	d

the formula for computing Yule's Q is

$$Q = \frac{ad - bc}{ad + bc}$$

(6.1)

Continuing the substantive example from Chapter 5, we have the following data:

	A	~A
C	37	2
~C	24	33

Inserting the appropriate information in 6.1, we achieve these results:

$$Q = \frac{(33)(37) - (2)(24)}{(33)(37) + (2)(24)} = .92$$

(6.2)

It will be recalled that the phi-square value for the same table was approximately .73; that is, the empirically determined chi-square equaled 73 per cent of the maximum value under a model of subimplication.

The meaning of Yule's Q is not clear. It should be observed that it may equal unity under a variety of conditions. These are, essentially, whenever a zero appears in the table. As we noted, this can occur in six different logical relations as alternatives to chance. Thus, in our example, we apparently have a high position relation. Yet I am not certain exactly how to appraise this particular statistic.

Thus, while mean-square contingency forced the assumption of an if-and-only-if model, Yule's Q seems to be too permissive. It approaches zero when ad = bc (the condition of randomness) or when a:c = b:d (the condition of equal proportions). Our knowledge of the relation between critical ratio and chi-square ought to prevent our being surprised at this. Yule's Q is most easily and most comfortably interpreted in the neighborhood of zero. Strong relations, however, require a return to the table from which the computations were made for safe interpretation. Since the table does not require a commitment to any logical relation prior to the test, it does not offer as rigorous a statement as phi-square. Of course, one may announce that he is using a particular model, employ Yule's Q, and obtain a coefficient; but this coefficient is not necessarily a measure of a fit.

When one says of Yule's Q that (as in our case) we have a 92 per cent association, one is left with the question: 92 per cent of what? There is no one answer to this question. Yule's Q is extremely easy to compute, but hard to interpret precisely.

The coefficient of contingency. An older measure of association, first suggested by Karl Pearson, is the coefficiency of contingency, denoted by C. The formula is

$$C = \sqrt{\frac{x^2}{x^2 + N}}$$

(6.3)

In applying this to our data, we recall that chi-square equaled 27.8 and N equaled 96. Inserting these in 6.3, we get

$$C = \sqrt{\frac{27.8}{27.8 + 96}} = \sqrt{\frac{27.8}{123.8}} = .474$$

(6.4)

If we note, however, that the absolute maximum which chi-square for a two-by-two table can obtain equals N, it is apparent that the upper limit of 6.3 is not equal to 1. Instead, we have

$$C = \sqrt{\frac{N}{N + N}} = \sqrt{\frac{1}{2}} = .707$$

(6.5)

This is a surprising result. For if statisticians can tolerate a measure of correlation, it must have unity as its upper limit. Accordingly, a correction is necessary. An obvious one is to divide 6.3 by the square root of ½. This corrected coefficient can achieve unity as its upper limit. Accordingly, we write

$$C' = \frac{C}{.707}$$

(6.6)

In our example, this correction would give us

$$C' = \frac{.474}{.707} = .67$$

(6.7)

which is close to the phi-square of .73. However, two things are missing. C' involved the extraction of a square root; so if we take the square root of phi-square, we find a degree of association equal to .85. Now the difference seems greater. Moreover, $C' = .67$ doesn't really say very much. That .67 is a middle range amount of association seems clear.

Recall that the computation of the coefficient of contingency involved a computation of chi-square. Thus the interpretation of C or C' is itself contingent upon an interpretation of chi-square. To take non-zero coefficients of contingency to be departures from chance is a loose way to interpret a statistic. And, as we have seen, the alternatives to chance vary considerably in their logical imputation.

The correction of C depended upon the conditions under which chi-square equaled N. We know that this is a stringent requirement. If we were to correct the coefficient for other maximum expectations, slightly different results would obtain. Thus, we may correct 6.5 in the following manner. Choose (from Chapter 5) the appropriate logical model. Insert the appropriate value for maximum chi-square in place of N in 6.5. In our case, this would be

$$C'' = \sqrt{\frac{x^2}{x^2 + \frac{n_1.n_{.2}}{n_{.1}n_2.}N}}$$

(6.8)

Now the maximum value of this will be ½; hence, it must be corrected as before. Thus

$$C''' = \frac{\sqrt{\frac{x^2}{x^2 + \frac{n_1.n_{.2}}{n_{.1}n_2.}N}}}{.707}$$

(6.9)

If we insert the appropriate numerical values in 6.9 we get

$$C''' = \frac{\sqrt{\frac{27.8}{27.8 + \frac{(39)(35)}{(61)(57)}96}}}{.707}$$

$$= \frac{\sqrt{\frac{27.8}{27.8 + 38}}}{.707}$$

$$= \frac{\sqrt{.422}}{.707}$$

$$= \frac{.648}{.707}$$

$$= .91$$

(6.10)

This result is much more similar to that obtained by Yule's Q than C′ which equaled .67. Not only is it extremely complicated, its interpretation is not much better than for Q. Fortunately, many statisticians suggest that the coefficient of contingency ought not be computed for anything less than a five-by-five table. Since C does not depend upon a unique logical model—the same value for χ^2 could come from a number of different sets of observations—the interpretation of the coefficient of contingency is always shaky.

This statistic can hardly be regarded as a serious contender for the space given to phi-square.

Tetrachoric correlation, r_t. Up to this point we have generally made use of "true" dichotomies. That is, we had the model of necessary and sufficient conditions in mind. This state of affairs limits us. What we need in addition is a measure of association for dichotomies flowing from one or more quantitatively defined measures. Such is the task of tetrachoric r.

The formula for its computation is forbidding, as we shall see. As a matter of fact, there are at least three methods for computing r. The first is approximate and very easy. Some restrictions are built into this method: the total number of cases in the table is large, the point of dichotomization is not too far toward the extreme ends of the distributions (which are normal and continuous), and the relationship is linear. We noted this last restriction on the median point of dichotomy for phi-square. If the table is not normal, the value of r_t is affected by the point at which the division was made.[1] Hence, one may provide a test of normalcy: move the point of division and note how stable the correlation coefficient is. If the dichotomy is essentially categorical, some rationalization would appear to be necessary.

The precise formula for the computation of tetrachoric r is very complicated. However, workable approximation is given in the following formula:

$$r_t = \frac{1}{ij}\left\{1 - \frac{1}{N}\sqrt{N^2 - \frac{2\,ij(bc - ad)}{IJ}}\right\}$$

(6.11)

i is found by computing either

$$\left(.5 - \frac{n_{.1}}{N}\right) \text{ or } \left(.5 - \frac{n_{.2}}{N}\right)$$

(6.12)

This gives the area under a normal curve bounded by the mean and x/σ; the numerical value for x/σ is i. j is found by computing either

$$\left(.5 - \frac{n_{1.}}{N}\right) \text{ or } \left(.5 - \frac{n_{2.}}{N}\right)$$

(6.13)

This gives the area under a normal curve bounded by the mean and x/σ; the numerical value for x/σ is j. Hence, in computing these values, one first obtains a percentage which is read in a table of the normal curve as area; then i or j is the corresponding x/σ value. I is the height of the ordinate at i; J is the height of the ordinate at j.

An alternative formula for 6.11 is the following:

$$r_t = -\cos\left[\frac{180° \sqrt{bc}}{\sqrt{ad} + \sqrt{bc}}\right]$$

(6.14)

However, since social scientists are more likely to be acquainted with the normal curve rather than with trigonometry, 6.11 will probably find more favor with them.

The conditions under which r_t equals zero require that $bc - ad = 0$. When this condition obtains, the term under the square-root sign equals N^2. Then the bracketed term equals $1 - N/N$, which is, of course, equal to zero. Hence, r would equal zero. The relation of tetrachoric r to Pearsonian r is shown in Figure 1. It is apparent from Figure 1 that the X and Y axes are normally distributed and that the relation is linear. The dots around the line are scatter, which is enclosed in the ellipses. The figure is cut into quadrants, not at the means. These are labeled as in a two-by-two table. It is clear that a positive linear relation requires *few* members of the a and d quadrants, and hence the ad term will be subtracted from the bc term (the reverse operation of the shortcut chi-square). If the relation is negative, the term under the square-root sign

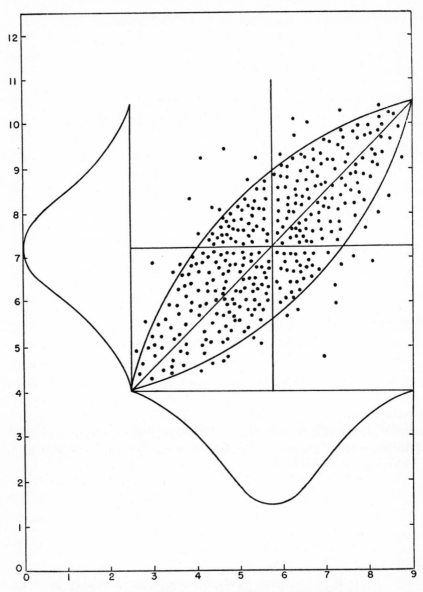

Figure 1. The relation of tetrachoric r to Pearsonian r

which includes $(ad - bc)$ will be added to N^2, and the square root of the resulting sum will be greater than N. This will result in $-r_t$ which signifies a negative relation. Care must be taken to insure the proper relation of increasing magnitudes in the tables of computation. In particular, if one dimension represents an unordered dichotomy, the sense of direction is really meaningless.

To illustrate the use of 6.11, we turn to a problem in migration. A cursory glance at American history will reveal the extent to which the development of this country has depended upon migration. From the westward expansion to the development of the city, natural increase has been insufficient to explain population growth. We need scarcely refer to the millions of people, born in Europe or elsewhere, who migrated to this country. All that we need do is to recognize that our cultural pattern includes a tradition of migration. Furthermore, to a greater or lesser degree, migration is a legitimate way to solve certain personal problems.

The phrase "to a greater or lesser degree" is, of course, a limp, vacuous statement without operational specification. In a recent research project, graduating seniors from a number of selected high schools in rural Minnesota were asked to approve or disapprove of a number of reasons for moving. These included such statements as "It is all right to move to avoid a bad reputation"; "It is all right to move to get away from a domineering family"; "It is all right to move to get out of paying debts"; and some fifteen other similar choices. The high schools were in two areas (for purposes of the present discussion), both in the cut-over section of the northern part of the state. One area is economically dependent upon mining and related industries; in the other farming and running resorts predominate. Is the number of approvals of reasons for moving correlated with the area where the students lived? The results are shown in Table 1.

Table 1. Number of Reasons for Moving Approved by High School Senior Boys, Classified by Area

No. of Approvals	Farming and Resort	Mining	Total
Six or fewer	150 (a)	121 (b)	271 $(n_{1.})$
Seven or more	168 (c)	210 (d)	378 $(n_{2.})$
Total	318 $(n_{.1})$	331 $(n_{.2})$	649 (N)

111

The computation of 6.11 requires the following information:

$i = .025$. $(.5 - 318/649) = .01$. This equals the area under the normal curve bounded by the mean and $i = .025$.

$I = .3988$. The height of the ordinate at this point is about .3988.

$j = .2$. $(.5 - 271/649) = .084$. This equals the area under the normal curve bounded by the mean and $j = 2$.

$J = .391$. The height of the ordinate at this point is about .391.

$ad = (150)(210)$.

$bc = (121)(168)$.

$N = 649$.

Inserting these in 6.11 we get the following:

$$r_t = \frac{1}{(.025)(21)}\left\{ 1 - \frac{1}{649}\sqrt{(649)^2 - \frac{(2)(.025)(.21)[(150)(210) - (121)(168)]}{(.3988)(.39)}} \right\}$$

(6.15)

From this point on, the matter is purely arithmetic. Whatever thinking is required ought to have preceded this step. The rest is mere technical detail. If we calculate correctly, we would get

$$r_t = \frac{1}{(.025)(.21)}\left[1 - \frac{649.6}{649} \right] = -.185$$

(6.16)

which is undoubtedly rather a low amount of correlation. If we interpret r_t as analogous to Pearsonian r, then the square of $-.18$ equals .0324, or slightly more than 3 per cent of the variance in number of approvals of reasons for migration as explained by an appeal to region. With 97 per cent of the variance left unaccounted for, the results are not impressive.

For comparative purposes, we shall compute Yule's Q by using 5.1. Thus

$$Q = \frac{(150)(210) - (121)(168)}{(150)(210) + (121)(168)} = \frac{11,172}{51,828} = .22$$

(6.17)

The difference in signs results from the way in which the two-by-two table is arranged to conform to the notion of linearity when computing r_t. The similarity in the asserted magnitude of relation is the point

I wish to call the reader's attention to. One of the reasons for this similarity is the underlying assumption of linearity in tetrachoric r and the relation between linearity and the if-and-only-if argument associated with the two-by-two table.

If one were faced with a relatively large number of correlations to compute (likely if one were attempting a factor analysis of a set of items in a test of some sort), some easier way of approximating correlation would be welcomed. Such a method is found in *Computing Diagrams for the Tetrachoric Correlation Coefficient* by L. Chesire, M. Saffir, and L. L. Thurstone. The test is found by reducing the frequencies in Table 1 to proportions of the total N (649) (see Table 2). If one must

Table 2. Data of Table 1 Changed to Proportions to Permit the Use of the Chesire, Saffir, and Thurstone Diagrams for Computing r_t

No. of Approvals	Farming and Resort	Mining	Total
Six or fewer	$(-).230$	$(+).186$	.416
Seven or more	$(+).260$	$(-).324$	.584
Total	.490	.510	1.000

compute a number of correlations involving the same total but a number of different tables, the easiest first step is to obtain the reciprocal of the total N:

$$\frac{1}{N} = \frac{1}{649} = .00154085$$

$$(6.18)$$

Then the frequencies are multiplied by this number to obtain the correct proportions. For example, we set up Table 2. Then we select either a column or a row whose total proportion is less than .50; we will let the row "Six or fewer" be a. Any column or row at right angles to a is b. The cell containing both a and b is denoted by c.

One then selects, from the book of diagrams, a diagram most closely approximating a. In our case, we take the diagram for $a = .42$ as shown in Figure 2. On the X axis, we read values for b. Letting $b = .490$, we find that $c = .23$. We extend a line from $c = .23$ to the right, and at right angles to the Y axis. We extend a line perpendicular to the X axis at $b = .490$. Where these lines cross, we read the approximate tetrachoric correlation coefficient. Although one normally does not really

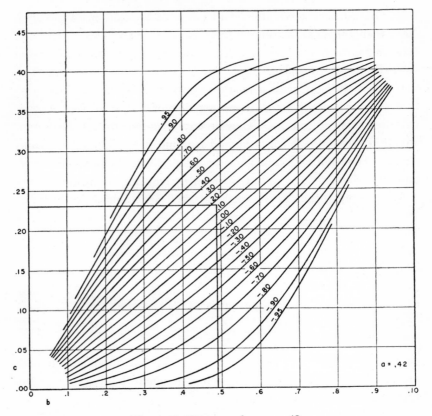

Figure 2. Diagram for a = .42

draw lines on the diagram—doing it mentally instead—I have done it here to illustrate in detail the technique. Note that we use lines which have a dimension, unlike the mathematics upon which the diagrams are based. This means that some error is always present, but it usually is not great.

In Table 2, we put in algebraic signs to indicate the quadrant in which the cell value falls. This is important in interpreting r_t. If the sign assigned to c is positive, one reads the correlation as it is in the diagram. But if c is negative (as it is in our example), one reverses the sign appearing in the table. Thus, although we read a positive correlation from the table, we affix a negative sign because our c was negative

When one has a large number of computations, it is easy to use a method such as this. The results are remarkably accurate. One further

114

note: the diagrams in Chesire, Saffir, and Thurstone's book are much larger than Figure 2. Accordingly, the amount of error is reduced. One's readings on the larger drawings are almost exactly approximate.

The important assumptions to bear in mind are these: the measure must be of normally distributed and continuous data, the relation must be linear. When these conditions are met, the interpretation usually given to the more commonly known Pearsonian r is altogether appropriate. And as we noted, the necessary and sufficient conditions idea is closely related to the idea of linearity. At least, when a strong linear relation is reduced to a two-by-two table, the similarity is striking.

Measuring success at prediction. One need not subscribe to the belief that the goal of science is prediction, and rejecting the belief does not imply a rejection of interest in prediction—which is, as we saw, a proper test for some empirical hypotheses.

Yet there are those who approach prediction as a purely technical question, to whom successful prediction epitomizes the clever scientist at work. Consider the example I have used previously from the study of a bureaucratic organization (p. 96).

	A	~A	t
C	37	2	39
~C	24	33	57
t	61	35	96

If one simply had 96 bureaucrats and were told to predict whether they were C or ~C the easiest thing would be to claim that they are all one or the other. If one asserted that they were all C, one would err 57 times out of 96. A smaller error would result from guessing that they were all ~C. The idea is to reduce this error to zero. Then someone says, "Well now, suppose that you knew that X of them were A's and N − X were ~A's; what would you predict from this knowledge?"

Continuing this line of thinking, a person may say, "All A's are C's." In doing so, he would err 24 times out of 61. If he were to say "No ~A's are C's," he would err only 2 times out of 35. This latter is, clearly, a good kind of argument, since his error must be reduced. But to what extent has the introduction of A and ~A reduced the error of prediction?

THE RHETORIC OF SCIENCE

This may be rephrased. One begins with a sample of S. He wants to say "All S are P." Alas, this is not true. The number of exceptions constitutes the error in his statement. Accordingly, some controls (A and ~A) are introduced. Proportionately, are there more A's which are C's than for the table as a whole? and, proportionately, are there more ~A's which are ~C's than for the table as a whole? All non-P for the total are regarded as error. Similarly, all non-P for the A's may be regarded as error and all P's for the ~A's may be regarded as error. The ideal, then, is to introduce a set of categories, A and ~A, hoping to get all the P's in one class and all the ~P's in the other. One may then want to see how close one came to this ideal.

A clever formula for determining this is[2]

$$\lambda_b = \frac{\Sigma_a P_{am} - P_{\cdot m}}{1 - P_{\cdot m}}$$

(6.19)

λ_b gives the proportion of errors that can be eliminated by taking A into account.

If all the values were in one cell, then this would be an indeterminate form. Actually, the task would be senseless if such were the case. λ_b ranges from 0 to 1; and is 0 if knowledge of the A class is of no help in predicting the C class, and is 1 if one of the diagonals equals unity. Although statistical independence implies a zero lambda, the converse is not true.

This tells us to add the largest cellular proportions in the two rows (ΣP_{am}) and subtract from this the largest proportion of a column marginal ($P_{\cdot m}$). This is then divided by the largest proportion of a column marginal. In our example the cell values to be added are .39 and .34; the column proportion is .64.

	A	~A	t
C	.39	.02	.41
~C	.25	.34	.59
t	.64	.36	1.00

$$\lambda_b = \frac{(.39 + .34) - .64}{1 - .64} = .25$$

116

This, it will be recalled, is remarkably similar to mean-square contingency; and this similarity probably stems from the fact that unity requires an if-and-only-if relation in both measures.

The severest criticism of this measure is its lack of theoretical grounding. It is strictly an *ad hoc* operation, and makes no appeal to previous research. As such, it does not include prediction as a test of relations. If it did so, it would have been able to take into account the fact that the essential task of prediction may well be the estimation of probabilities.[3] On the basis of previous research, it may be estimated (for example) that the proportion of *A*'s which are *C*'s is .60, and the proportion of the $\sim A$'s which are *C*'s is .06. Then one may use these proportions as estimations of probabilities in subsequent research. Whether or not these column proportions recur in the future will determine the extent to which one may predict the number of members in the C class for the entire table. Note that this view of prediction will allow for (a) "true" probabilities and (b) varying numbers of members in the A and $\sim A$ classes such that the total proportions may change over time.

In short, the technique of measuring prediction based upon 5.1 necessarily requires perfect measurement as a goal. It fails to relate to theory, and does not take into account the likelihood of estimating probabilities from research. As a technical device, for those interested in technique, the argument is perfectly sensible. But for those who envisage a theory encompassing probability statements, the device has little to offer. This is probably the trouble with viewing prediction as a technical rather than as a theoretical issue.

Jahn's index of segregation. As an illustration of the way in which a theoretical point of view can modify a statistical argument, we shall consider Jahn's index of segregation.[4] Representation in a two-by-two table would be as follows:

	Membership in ethnic groups (perfect segregation)	
	Majority	Minority
Residence in ethnic areas:		
Majority		0
Minority	0	

According to this, a member of the majority group who lives in an area for the minority is an error; and a member of the minority group who lives in the areas for the majority is also an error. Note that this does not allow for those relationships in which the member of the majority may invade the social life of the minority. The model requires a complete separation. Hence it is of only limited applicability. But anyone can insert other limiting conditions and invent a similar measure.

At any rate, the extent of segregation can be sensibly measured. To use Jahn's technical vocabulary, "values of the index are equal to the difference between the observed and the maximum possible error or reproducibility as a proportion of the maximum error." The maximum error must be the number equal to the population of the minority group: if half this number lived in white areas and a similar number of whites lived in Negro areas, there would be no residential segregation of whites and Negroes. This leads us to the form of the index. Using the symbols we have used in tabular representation,

$$I_s = \frac{n_{.2} - (b + c)}{n_{.2}}$$

(6.20)

with the symbols as in this two-by-two table

	A	~A	t
C	a	b	n_1.
~C	c	d	n_2.
t	$n_{.1}$	$n_{.2}$	

The following representation shows the estimated number of persons in Seattle, Washington in 1947, classified by ethnic group and ethnic area.[5]

Ethnic area:	White	Nonwhite	Total
White	377,349	5,106	382,455
Nonwhite	2,804	16,460	19,264
Total	380,153	21,566	401,719

118

Inserting the appropriate terms in 6.20, we get

$$I_s = \frac{21,566 - (2,804 + 5,106)}{21,566} = .63$$

$$(6.21)$$

The implication is that Seattle, in 1947, was 63 per cent segregated. Of course, whether this is a proper measurement of segregation is probably questionable. Certainly, some may feel that measuring segregation requires more than just a formal arrangement of frequencies. Something like sanctions imposed upon the errors would seem to be required by at least some theories of race relations. That is another matter.

At the moment, it may be interesting to note the similarities between this measure and other proposed measures. Our preceding measure, lambda, would be found to be

$$\lambda_b = \frac{(.945 + .04) - .95}{1 - .95} = .70$$

$$(6.22)$$

and Yule's Q would be:

$$Q = \frac{(377,349)(16,460) - (5,106)(2,804)}{(377,349)(16,460) + (5,106)(2,804)} = .99$$

$$(6.23)$$

This latter is clearly overestimating something. Note how one cell alone contains almost 95 per cent of the total number of cases. Clearly, λ_b is a better measure. I_s, being so similar in magnitude to λ_b is easier to compute, which may be in its favor.

CHAPTER 7

An Attempt to Measure Causality

WESTERN man has long searched for a causal explanation of the world about him.[1] Various interpretations have been made of the idea of cause. The Aristotelian are probably the best known. One reason for this lies in Aristotle's having pushed cause back to "first cause" and "purpose."

Proving cause is another matter. When modern man began to develop empirical science, authority was thrown overboard. Some felt they heard the baby splash too. The goal of this overthrow of authority was a completely objective point of view, permitting no subjective processes on the part of the scientist. Certainly this overthrow did result in the development of a technique, and many a laboratory assistant could serve as another eye or arm of the scientist. Eventually, science began to be thought of entirely as method. But still, calling electronic computing devices brains could only be a cynical joke or the epitome of nonhuman, thoughtless scientism.

The cry for objective methods corresponds with a view of the world, especially the relation of man to knowing the world. Man was regarded as essentially a passive agent; indeed, any mental activity was "subjective" and impossible to replicate. The world beamed stimuli at the observer. If he were equipped with the proper set of tools, these stimuli could be apprehended without error. Moreover, these stimuli impinged upon man's senses, *causing* a neural reaction. From the time of Hume, sophisticated men talked about habit of perception as being the closest one could come to cause. Cause could not be *seen*, hence cause could not be asserted.

During the later phases of the history of this way of thinking, statistical inference began to rear its ugly head. Here was a logic that enabled one to make assertions about less than certainty. A theory of chance was developed in such a way that under certain conditions chance could not sensibly explain the observation in question. This posed a dilemma. For if chance could not explain the observation, did this not mean that cause was present? Apparently, one had considered a strong alternative of a random world or a (causally) determined world. Should not the rejection of chance force the inference of cause?

The statistician Pearson said no: all that could be asserted was association. Almost a generation earlier John Stuart Mill had argued that concomitant variation was a proof of cause or something intimately connected to cause. Pearson rejected this position. Statistical analysis gave no proof of cause. All one could talk about was association.

A more precise formulation would have been something like the following. A rejection of chance allows one to talk at *least* about association. Now, the technically minded statistician is likely to pose such problems as: "If you had to predict whether S was or was not C, and all you knew was that it was S, what would you predict?" Later, such statisticians may ask, "Since you did as badly as chance, what would you predict if that S was C?" Apparently, all one is given to work with is an actuarial table or the barest table from which some interesting statistic could be computed.

A scientist usually has more knowledge than that. His technical assistant—a statistical clerk who computes the things he is told to compute—may be given only the information contained in the barest of tables. But the *scientist* has access to more knowledge than that. Of course, if the scientist is passive, he may lie awake, waiting for his data to say something. On the other hand, the scientist may be aware that his categories have relations to other ideas of the discipline than those asserted in the table. The scientist may have a category of asserted taste in music; he may associate this with, say, preference for a particular program. Let us assume that the association was beyond the range of chance. Does the scientist wish to infer that the fact of having asserted a taste in music generates a preference for a particular program? That probably would smell of causality, and he would say, "No, these are simply two different behaviors that are associated." Yet one knows that a verbal commitment may lead to a specific type of behavior because of the commitment alone.

The point of view which we took is that cause is not a thing. It is not beaming sense impressions upon the eye or the ear or whatever. To pose the problem of looking to see something is to have a naive view of the world, and of the scientist's relation to knowledge. Cause is a relation. Whether a given statistical table permits an inference of cause depends entirely upon the operational specifications given to the term. These, in turn, depend upon the theoretical dimensions given to the terms involved in the definition of cause.

Our operational specifications will never be completely without error. We must therefore use a probabilistic statement. Hence, if one requires certainty in a formulation of cause, cause can never be asserted. Certainty is probably the basis of most of the discussion of cause, for what was lacking in previous empirical discussions of cause was proof. Instead of inquiring into the meaning that could sensibly be attached to proof, earlier thinkers discussed instead what cause is. This issue of proof is involved in three other related topics: induction, explanation, and the formation of concepts.

I reject induction as a set of rules for insuring discovery. Rather, I prefer to retain the word as meaning the process of developing some new idea relating to an explanation of some problem. Induction is intimately connected with the ad hoc analysis. It can never be used as proof, since it necessarily must involve a finite number of objects and, usually, a tiny proportion of all possible cases. In the same way as it is related to the ad hoc analysis, induction is related to the formation of concepts. It is not necessary to believe that a passive mind after carefully being bombarded by technically corrected stimuli will necessarily shape itself to correspond with reality. In short, it is not necessary to believe that forming concepts is a special case of reducing error in the sense that a rat in a maze reduces error.

This leads us to a concern with explanation. I doubt that a high degree of association is, in itself, an explanation of anything. For one thing, association, if it has any meaning at all, must be unable to distinguish between what is theoretically an antecedent and what is theoretically a consequent. Before explanation is achieved, association must be shown to be a necessary consequent of the theoretical meanings attached to that which is associated. That is, there must be some reason for the association. This reason is usually a principle or a law which is essentially an approved guide for drawing inferences. One kind of connection of principle may be terms causal, which requires a theoretical distinction between an antecedent and a consequent.

In any event, some connecting principle is enunciated. If this principle is true, then certain consequences must also be true. One devises a test to determine the truth of these consequences. If the inference is sustained in fact, the principle is sustained. If the inference is falsified, so is the principle upon which it is based. Hence, it is within the sense of theory-formation to hold that a causal hypothesis must contain implications which are testable. It is the inference which is tested. The term verification indicates (a) an inability to falsify the premise upon which the research rests and (b) the unwillingness of anyone to assert proof in the sense of final certainty. Our logic does not warrant proving anything (unless "to prove" is taken in the sense of "to test").

A simple-minded way of estimating the amount of cause. If chance and cause are at least contraries, then a table showing less than certainty but more than chance ought to generate a statistic with the same characteristics. The amount of cause present in the tabular representation of the data must be less than one hundred per cent, but more than zero per cent. As a matter of fact, a measure of causality may be held to show the extent to which data go beyond a chance distribution.[2] The germ of the idea is this: *absence of cause does not imply zero members; it implies a chance distribution.* Hence, one can propose a measure of perfect cause and also a measure of perfect chance and observe the extent to which one's data depart from chance in the direction of cause. Note that this is a formal, not a substantive, argument.

The operations of the proposed measure are as follows: (a) Locate the cell with the fewest numbers; call this s. (b) Determine the *expected* frequency of this cell, denoted by $_sf_t$. Now, the absolute difference in magnitude between what is observed and what is expected by chance is the same for all cells. This is the absolute amount of deviation beyond chance. For the given marginal totals, how much more could chance have been reduced? Obviously, the maximum reduction would have been $_sf_t$ since negative frequencies are not allowed. An argument which comes readily to mind would be to divide the amount chance had been

123

reduced by the maximum amount it could have been reduced. Symbolically

$$D = \frac{_sf_t - s}{_sf_t} = 1 - \frac{s}{_sf_t}$$

$$(7.1)$$

Applying this to our example of bureaucratic behavior, we get

		Is		
		A	~A	t
Ought:	C	37	2	39
	~C	24	33	57
	t	61	35	96

Clearly, s equals 2; $_sf_t$ equals 39 times 35 divided by 96 or 14.22. Inserting these into 7.1, we get

$$D = 1 - \frac{2}{14.22} = .86$$

$$(7.2)$$

This means that 86 per cent of the *possible* displacement of the frequency expected by chance has occurred. Evidently a strong relation exists. Note that this is similar to the results obtained by earlier methods, especially those that do not demand if-and-only-if relations.

Yet nothing about cause can be asserted. If the hypothetical relation demanded by theory is that of cause, then we have 86 per cent of maximum cause. This does not warrant our saying that 86 per cent of the cause is explained, because cause is a kind of relation, not a set of forces.

D can equal unity when any cell equals zero; D can equal zero when the smallest frequency equals a chance expectancy. Although the first statement seems ambiguous, the latter makes good sense. For if chance is contrary to cause, then the amount of cause ought to equal zero when chance is a sufficient explanation. This should come as no great surprise. After all, this was how we defined our measure in the first place.

For a symmetrical table, we would compute the average D for the two columns. One type of average is simple: Add the two D's and divide by two. The other is simple but involves a less well known average (the geometric mean): take the square root of the product of the column D's.

The latter is possible only if D does not equal zero for either column.

McCormick's kappa-prime. At a time when the popular thing for a statistician to do was to invent predictive gimmicks, McCormick posed another problem. Granting that a particular table may arrange the data in such a way that error could be reduced from that implied by the marginal totals, how stable would such a tabular arrangement be? What kind of guarantee is there that the same table would generate an equal reduction of error the next time it was used? There is none, as long as mere association is present: "correlation analysis can be made much more effective for predictive purposes if at the same time some attention is paid to the principles of causation."[3]

One of the difficulties resides in the fact that the social scientist is not likely to be studying a rigorously controlled experiment Rather, he is more likely to be studying events as they occur. Not only that, but the scientist has but a small part of the whole universe of events. He samples a universe of some kind. To imagine that but one kind of universe exists is to make a grievous mistake.

It is also important to notice whether the universe to be sampled is to be regarded as a *unique*, historical set of events (situation), as a *constant* or *recurrent* situation or system of causes, or as a *changing* situation. If we are interested in the death rate from the influenza epidemic of 1918, we have a unique universe. But if we attempt to predict the rate of mortality in Chicago, we assume a continuous or recurrent, i.e., essentially unchanging, universe. As a matter of fact, strictly continuous or recurrent universes never occur in social research, since there is constant change in the complex of factors that compose any social situation. The important question, therefore, is whether the universe can be expected to be approximately recurrent, or unchanged, over a period in which we are interested. If so, we may be justified in trying to predict what will happen in that period on the strength of what has occurred. It is sometimes possible to discover the nature, direction, and rate of change in a changing universe, so that we can allow for it in making a prediction.[4]

The kind of universe sampled will necessarily have an effect upon the kind of prediction made. An initial operation, then, will be to define the universe. Notice how all the various definitions of universe require some notion of cause. Indeed, the universe seems to be composed of different kinds of causal systems—unique ones, recurring ones, and changing ones.

Clearly, the causal system appealed to in an experiment is usually a recurring one, although a changing one may be constructed. It is one thing to develop a predictive argument based upon a controlled experiment. It is quite another to use that information to predict what will happen in a different causal system (i.e., the world of everyday behavior). Unless one has knowledge of causal relationships, success in that sort of predictive enterprise would depend upon chance.

McCormick sees no set of rules for finding causes.

The art of discovering causal relationships depends first on familiarity with particular data, then on trying all likely causal conditions that suggest themselves, and screening them down to the smallest effective number.[5]

What one evidently does is to get some ideas as to what causes are likely to exist and then test the consequences of these proposed causes. How one gets these causal conditions (unless they patiently suggest themselves) is not known. This seems a rather uninteresting subject. Of more importance is developing a method of screening them down to the smallest effective number. The essential logic can best be shown in a contingency table.

Using the example of voting behavior as the thing to be explained, McCormick attempts to measure the causal relation between voting behavior and intent to vote. Prediction of voting behavior from statements of intent is justified "only if such statements are causally related to voting behavior."[6] Whether causally related means that the fact of asserting a particular intent was the cause of a particular vote, or whether asserting and voting are both caused by the same thing, is not clear. The connection must be justified by "social-psychological or other relevant causal theory."[7]

In an experience table, the rows designate the events to be explained. The columns denote the causes. These must be arranged so that the same

characteristics or causal conditions are presumably present in only one column and absent from all others; and the members of the sample are distributed among the columns according to their characteristics.[8]

However, one should not imagine that a column designates only one cause. Many undefined causal conditions are likely to be more or less present.

It is accordingly always necessary to think in terms of the results of a defined column causal system and its unspecified causal associates, rather than in terms of the former alone.[9]

It seems apparent that the notion of cause is fundamental to the argument. But exactly what does cause mean? At first, McCormick denies any attempt to get involved in any philosophical argument over the meaning and reality of a cause. But he gives the following operational specification:

If the presence of a condition or set of conditions is always followed by the presence of a particular event in a column of a table, there is indication that the condition or set may be invariably a *sufficient* determiner or cause of the event. If the absence of a condition or set of conditions is always followed by the absence of a particular event in a column, there is indication that the condition or set may be invariably a *necessary* determiner or cause of the event.[10]

It is evident that this corresponds to an earlier idea of cause as described by Mill in his canons of agreement and difference and in the subsequent discussion of necessary and sufficient conditions. Of particular interest is the implicit assumption, which I now make explicit, *that cause is a primitive concept in science.* What it is is a matter of philosophical debate; the scientist merely takes cause as something necessary for stable prediction. One may proceed to measure it, to label different kinds of it. But to define it—this is not necessary; it is a primitive idea.

This means that one must attach causal theory to some substantive branch of inquiry, say social-psychological theory, before he begins causal analysis. After such connection has been made, the problem becomes essentially determining the amount of confidence which can be placed in an experience table. Apart from the usual requirements of a random sample of adequate size, one must (a) determine the statistical significance of a relationship within a table; (b) assess the evidence that the relationship is that of sufficient and necessary cause and effect; (c) determine the power of the table to predict individual behavior under stable causal conditions. This last condition arises from the assumption that cause means certainty and absence of error.[11]

To facilitate discussion, I shall use a modification of McCormick's example.[12] The facts of life are contained in the following experience table. D means Democrat, R means Republican. We need not doubt here the likelihood of these being truly recurring categories; the issue is merely technical.

	Intended to vote		
	D	R	t
Voted:			
D	125	40	165
R	20	150	170
t	145	190	335

(a)

The first task is to determine whether chance is a sufficient explanation for this table. Using the traditional shortcut method, we obtain

$$\chi^2 = \frac{[(125)(150) - (40)(20)]^2\, 335}{(145)(190)(165)(170)} = 139.18$$

(7.3)

And, obviously, chance may be safely rejected.

We turn now to determining the amount of evidence that the relationship is a necessary and sufficient cause and effect. In the computation of χ^2 the row totals were utilized. However, in measuring the extent to which the table represents a departure from chance, the row totals have no significance. Indeed, the row totals, according to McCormick, "are merely by-products of the systems of causal forces that operate within the columns of an experience table."[13] Hence, the proper allocation of chance requires that the column total should be divided by the number of rows. This necessitates the argument that, within a column, if chance is a pure operator, an object has equal probability of falling into any row designations. Accordingly, the table below shows the maximum distribution of "pure chance."

	Intended to vote	
	D	R
Voted:		
D	73	95
R	72	95
t	145	190

(b)

We need, also, a representation of a maximum distribution of cause—or maximum predictive efficiency. From the foregoing discussion, it is apparent that the minor diagonal will contain zeros. Relinquishing the row totals makes this possible.

The table for maximum predictive efficiency is

	Intended to vote	
	D	R
Voted:		
D 145		0
R 0		190
t 145		190

The measure of causal efficiency is developed as follows:

The absolute sum of the differences between the cell frequencies of [a] and [b] represents the departure of the minimum model from the maximum model, whereas the absolute sum of the differences between the cell frequencies of [a and b] and [b] represents the actual departure of [a] from the same maximum. The ratio of the two absolute sums of differences will be an index of the relative departure of [b] from maximum efficiency.[14]

For the two tables as a whole,

$$\kappa = \frac{(20 + 20) + (40 + 40)}{72 + 72 + 95 + 95} = .65$$

(7.4)

In two-by-two tables like those we have used thus far (see p. 73),

$$\kappa = \frac{1 - 2(b + c)}{N}$$

(7.5)

This is not a completely satisfactory measure, however, since some tables may represent a situation in which one set of conditions may be much greater than the other. Accordingly, one ought to develop a measure which does not make causality dependent upon the number of members in a given causal system within a column. That is to say, a preferred measure will give equal weight to the columns making up the experience table. Defining p as the number of members in the class required by the idea of necessary and sufficient conditions divided by the number of members of the columnary category, the measure kappa-prime would be, for any column j having r rows, where m is the number of columns

$$\kappa'_j = \frac{(rp_j - m)}{(r-1)m}$$

(7.6)

and for the two-by-two table as a whole

$$\kappa' = \frac{a}{n_{.1}} - \frac{b}{n_{.2}} = p_A - p_A$$

(7.7)

In the example cited,

$$\kappa' = \frac{125}{145} - \frac{40}{190} = .655$$

(7.8)

This, then, completes the statistical requirements of the measure of causal efficiency. Kappa-prime, particularly, has some interesting characteristics. It is freed from both row and column totals. These, after all, may be regarded as being quite accidental to the causal system under investigation. The measure is achieved by defining maximum predictive efficiency and minimum predictive efficiency for the data presented for analysis. The difference between the observed cell frequencies and what would obtain under maximum predictive efficiency must mean less than perfect causal control. This number as a ratio of the difference between the minimum and maximum condition is the percentage of causal efficiency lost in the operational specifications of the causal conditions. Unity minus the percentage lost gives the required measure. If the data represent the chance distribution as defined by the relinquishment of row totals, kappa equals zero. One is not likely ever to compute a kappa-prime equal or nearly equal to zero, since a test of independence will have preceded this step. If there is no difference between the postulated perfect model and the actual experience table, kappa must equal unity.

Some general comments. In his general argument, McCormick held that for causal analysis, one must have a square table.[15] The two-by-two table is, of course, square; so the problem did not properly emerge in the presentation of kappa for the two-by-two table.

The assertion that the table must be square or be meaningless is a strong assertion. We must inquire into McCormick's justification for it.

Elsewhere in this volume, I have discussed the difference between a plurality of causes and multiple causation; the latter can well be incorporated into McCormick's position. If by the former we mean that a given event (say, divorce) may be caused by a number of different conditions, McCormick disagrees. He refuses to hold that sufficiency of causality is related to plural causes.

Had he held to the doctrine of plurality of causes, he would have agreed that for an experience of r rows there must be at least r columns. This notion he seems to reject: "This is because one 'divorce' or 'delinquency' is not just the same as another." [16] Hence, in any proposed system of causal explanations, if more than one cause is offered, the effect must be redefined. Yet he writes, "The position is taken here that research experience has amply demonstrated that many, if not all, events which sociologists are interested in predicting . . . may be the result of more than one system of causes." [17] The seeming confusion comes from a strange statement: "Furthermore, a table in which every column contains a completely sufficient cause will automatically contain necessary causes, also, so far as that table is concerned." [18] What he is actually saying is that *in a causal analysis, it is not sufficient that one adduce a cause for a problematic event; one must adduce causes for every alternative outcome.* Under this condition, he is right: sufficiency implies necessity because all outcomes are sufficiently explained.

Accordingly, one may reject the requirement that the table must be square. This rejection can stem from two premises. One is that it is proper to seek a number of sufficient causes for the same outcome. The second is that one need not adduce a sufficient cause for each possible outcome. A residual category of unexplained material may, to some, be quite proper.

Kappa, as defined in the cited article, is appropriate only for square tables. Hence, a rejection of the requirements of a square table seems to imply a rejection of kappa and its companion correction, kappa-prime.

Yet the general argument which McCormick developed is not restricted to the square table; only the formulae are restricted. The logic of his argument is altogether independent of his assertions about sufficiency and necessity. Without proposing a formula, which could be easily written since it would be only a symbolic representation of the arithmetic operations, we shall remind ourselves of what the general argument actually was.

The first step is the creation of an experience table. This is a simple empirical categorization of the data to be explained. Then one may create a model of minimum predictive efficiency, in precisely the same way as McCormick suggested. The creation of a table of maximum predictive efficiency may present some difficulties; the retention of plural causes may prove embarrassing. Yet if proposed cause A_1 is different from proposed cause A_2 and if both are completely sufficient to cause the effect, both A_1 and A_2 will have zeros for all outcomes other than the effect in question.

	A_1	A_2	$\sim(A_1VA)_2$
C	1	1	0
$\sim$C	0	0	1

If one observes this in a table, he is likely to imagine that A_1 and A_2 are not really different, after all. Their difference ought not be a matter of ad hoc assertion.

I have some difficulty in accepting the argument that one must predict the behavior of individuals. Moreover, I cannot accept the implicit assumption that perfect causal expression is feasible. Yet nothing, as far as I now understand it, prevents kappa and kappa-prime from being consistent with the latter modification. However, if perfect causal expression is not feasible, then one can never perfectly predict behavior of individuals. At some point, analysis must report probabilities; and it will be impossible to determine whether these probabilities correspond to a peculiar real world, or result from errorful operational specifications.

Some comparisons with other measures. Kappa-prime gave us the value of .655, while kappa generated approximately .65. The similarity of the two measures results from the similarity of numbers of people intending to vote the two tickets. In general, this says that the empirical distribution achieved 65 per cent of the difference between pure chance and pure cause, as defined in the text.

Lambda, the measure of predictive efficiency, generated these results:

$$\lambda = \frac{(.37 + .45) - .57}{1 - .57} = .58$$

$$(7.9)$$

This allows one to say that knowledge of intent increased the guess of the outcome by 58 per cent of what was possible.

132

Phi-square, a measure dependent upon chi-square, and hence upon the magnitude of both marginal totals, gives the result

$$\phi^2 = \frac{139.18}{335} = .42$$

(7.10)

This may be stated in the following way: the empirical chi-square (which warranted a rejection of chance) is 42 per cent of the maximum chi-square implied by perfect necessary and sufficient conditions. It differs from kappa in that it uses the row marginal totals for the definition of chance.

Yule's Q gives the largest value:

$$Q = \frac{(125)\,(150) - (40)\,(20)}{(125)\,(150) + (40)\,(20)} = .90$$

(7.11)

It is not exactly clear just what can be said on the basis of this. Certainly a feeling of a strong relation is warranted.

The second section of this chapter (p. 124) closed with the statement of two simple-minded measures of beyond chance. These required obtaining averages of D, as defined by 7.1. One value, D_a, involving an arithmetic mean, is obtained by

$$D_a = \frac{D_a + D_{\sim a}}{2}$$

where the subscripts denote the column designations. Inserting the proper values in this equation, we get

$$D_a = \frac{(.73 + .35)}{2} = .54$$

(7.12)

The other value for the average D, denoted by D_g, involving a geometric mean, is obtained by

$$D_g = \sqrt{D_a D_{\sim a}}$$

(7.13)

where the subscripts have the same meaning. Inserting the proper numbers in this equation, we get

$$D_g = \sqrt{(.73)\,(.35)} = .505$$

(7.14)

THE RHETORIC OF SCIENCE

These results are quite similar, apparently in the same neighborhood as lambda and phi. Their interpretation does not add much knowledge: the percentage by which chance expectancy was displaced.

If 7.12 and 7.13 are simple-minded, the following measure is even more so. One may observe that the members of the main diagonal were correctly predicted, that members of the minor diagonal are errors. One may ask simply, "What percentage of all members were correctly predicted?" This can be obtained by summing the main diagonal and dividing by N,

$$I = \frac{a+d}{N}$$

(7.15)

The empirical value of this is found by

$$I = \frac{125+150}{335} = .82$$

Apparently, 82 per cent of the voters were properly placed. This does not take into account anything except what is given in the table. Had necessary and sufficient conditions been present, it, too, would have equaled unity. So would they all.

In the limits, all of the measures equal unity or zero. They all require different operations (in the sense of calculations); they usually require different interpretations of how one measures the extremes of chance and cause. Lambda, I, and Yule's Q are largely technical in orientation. Phi-square, D, and I require notions of chance in their interpretation. Phi-square and D use the same definition of chance. Phi-square, however, uses chi-square as a measure of perfect association. D uses the difference between the expected and observed frequency as its fundamental idea. Kappa, like D, goes beyond chance; like phi-square, it requires a model table. It differs markedly in its formulation of chance. At least, it is freed from row totals; these are regarded as mere accidents associated with arithmetic. Apparently, the choice of a measure will depend upon how one defines chance; and this, apparently, depends upon what one means by cause.

CHAPTER 8

Correlated Dichotomies and the Problem of Joint Effects

STATISTICALLY oriented social scientists dream of model-building. Theoretically oriented social scientists dream of paradigm-building. And though they may end by creating the same thing, the paradigm is certainly the fancier of the two; three-syllable words are always to be preferred in social science writing. Were it not for the polysyllabic vocabularies entrenched in the various disciplines, members of one field might discern what was being done in others. And then where would intellectual empires be?

Seriously, or at least noticeably more seriously than the previous paragraph would suggest, the creation of ideographic devices aids in the extension of ideas beyond the present confines. As a heuristic gimmick, the two-by-two table has a long and varied history. Much can be said for it on that basis alone. Consider, for example, the way in which it can facilitate the construction of types.[1] Let us have two dichotomous dimensions: age and relative safety in driving. A tabular representation would be:

	Old	*Young*
Safe	a	b
Unsafe	c	d

Obviously one can immediately build four types: (a) the old, safe driver; (b) the young, safe driver; (c) the old, unsafe driver; (d) the young, unsafe driver.

Although we have, up to this point (and we shall again later), used the two-by-two table for purposes of assessing association, this need not be the use of the table. Much of science is devoted to explaining different arrangements. In this case, a question would be, Is it possible that one or more of these types is much rarer than any of the others?

Although the question may be raised, a researcher may not necessarily wish to raise the question. Instead, he may ask, What are the consequences of this particular conjunction of factors? What implications follow from the observation of the type "young, unsafe driver"?

In rural sociology, to change the example, one may classify county farming patterns according to whether they are mechanized or not; and, again, as to whether the farming pattern is dangerous (high accidental death rate) or not. One may wonder if mechanization is related to the high accidental death rate: but one may also wonder, irrespective of the kind of relationship, what results obtain for the county which represents a particular kind of pattern. It may well be that low mechanization is not *causally* related to a high accident rate. Yet important consequences may indeed follow upon the chance connection of these characteristics.

For a third example, consider certain population statistics. Dichotomously define counties as high in percentage of population over 65 and low on the same measure. Also define the counties as low in percentage of population under 5, and high on the same measure. It may well be that the two measures are randomly connected; it does not matter. Indeed, it may be that high over 65 tends to be associated with low under 5 throughout a state or region. Then consider the rare combination of high over 65 and high under 5. Obviously, some highly practical considerations flow from this conjunction (and, to the alert observer, something of theoretical interest). For one thing, this kind of county has a larger than average proportion of its population in the nonproductive age groups. The burden of a county to care for its aged and to prepare to educate its young poses a number of problems. How they are resolved —how they are perceived by the residents of the area—is of interest to sociology, in particular. The point is simple: one need not always propose an explanation of a typology implied by a two-by-two table. The problem could certainly be in discerning what difference this makes.

The use of the two-by-two table in depicting a typological system ought not to be treated too casually. Too often, it would seem, a great deal of potential usefulness has been neglected. Consider, for example, the task of attempting to determine which logical model is required by current theory. Suppose that one is assessing the relation between statements of the adequacy of laws covering negligence and statements assessing the existence of a social problem of fatal farm accidents. Here we may create the following table:

	Laws	
	Adequate	Inadequate
Accidents:		
A problem	a	b
Not a problem	c	d

The task is now to assess the possibility of any type's occurring and the relative likelihood of each type's occurring. The reason for the first is to determine whether or not the definition of terms logically denies the existence of a particular type.

a. *Laws covering negligence are adequate, but accidents are a problem.* Is this a sensible statement to make? Under what conditions is it possible for both statements to be true? If the enforcement mechanism is lacking for any reason, both could be true. In particular, if the members of the community refuse to assist the law enforcement agency, it is possible to fix the difficulty upon the attitudes of the members of the society. This is apparently what is assumed by much of the current anti-auto-accident propaganda.

b. *Laws covering negligence are inadequate, and there is a problem.* This seems like a natural response, especially if one believes that laws solve social problems. From this point of view a law that needs correction suggests that a problem exists, or there would be no problem. It is possible, moreover, to feel that there is no connection between the adequacy of laws covering negligence and the number of farm accidents, to believe that the laws happen to be inadequate and the number of farm accidents is so great that a problem does exist. One may make this response on two bases: (1) an assumed relation between laws about negligence and problems of fatal accidents, or (2) an assumed independence of the two, although an appraisal of fact shows that the two parts of the statement are true.

c. *Laws covering negligence are adequate, and there is no problem.* This makes almost immediate sense. Of course, it would be possible to take this position if one believed that there were relatively few accidents or that the laws were so well enforced that everything was under control.

d. *Laws covering negligence are inadequate, but there is no problem.* At first, it might seem that these two ideas are contradictory. But recall that the accidents are farm fatalities. A person might well believe that laws covering negligence are more appropriate to an urban environment and of no consequence to the rural area where each farmer is an independent individual with no legal obligation to others where accidents are concerned. Moreover, an argument similar to b could be appealed to.

Clearly, all four types are possible. They are not necessarily equally probable; judgment of this will give an idea of which logical model is appropriate. Doubtless types b and c are likely to be the most frequently used. The task then is to assess the relative frequencies of a and d. What this requires is an effort to determine the frequency of the conditions under which the two types could be true. If the judgment that the laws are adequate and that this is independent of the existence of a social problem occurs more frequently than the judgment that enforcement mechanisms are inefficient, then type a would occur least often. This would produce the following table:

	Laws	
	Adequate	Inadequate
Accidents:		
A problem	a→0	b
Not a problem	c	d

If we can agree to regard statements about the adequacy of laws as being antecedents, the relationship is seen to be subcontrariety. Were one to use phi-square as a measure of association, the form would be

$$\phi^2 = \frac{(ad - bc)^2}{(n_1.)(n._1)}$$

$$(8.1)$$

138

CORRELATED DICHOTOMIES AND JOINT EFFECTS

Examples could be multiplied almost endlessly. The point is simple. The two-by-two table can be used to specify the interesting types. One may then try to develop a priori estimates regarding the possibility and subsequently the probability of each of the four types. In doing this, one can determine a model of logical relations to test.

The chi-square of correlated proportions. Up to now, we have discussed the problem of independent samples. These are not likely to exhaust the kinds of problems a researcher may face. Two obvious situations not covered by the preceding analysis are the before-and-after study and the response of the same sample to a number of items. I present an example of the latter.

In the research on bureaucracy,[2] 96 workers in a federal employment agency were asked paired questions about office practices. Their responses were dichotomously defined as being bureaucratic and nonbureaucratic. One item of the pair related to what the person believed actually was the case, the other to what the person believed ought to be the case. In response to a question about the rules governing official behavior, 61 out of the 96 said that the rules were bureaucratic, only 39 out of the 96 said that the rules ought to be bureaucratic. Is the proportion different? It would seem that more of the employees said that the rules were bureaucratic than said that they needed to be. What is the statistical significance of this?

We saw earlier that the critical ratio of proportions could be assessed in the form of a two-by-two table. Accordingly, it may occur to some that one could develop the following table:

	Is	Ought	Total
Like a bureaucracy	61	39	100
Not like a bureaucracy	35	57	92
Total	96	96	192

A calculation of chi-square would result in

$$x^2 = \frac{(61)(57) - (35)(39)^2 \, 192}{(96)(96)(100)(92)} = 10.01$$

(8.2)

Because of the obvious symmetry in the table, the amount of association could be measured by

$$\phi^2 = \frac{10.01}{192} = .05$$

which is extremely low.

Of course, the whole exercise is faulty. Two glaring errors exist. Note how the total size doubled—each individual was included twice. Moreover, the amount of correlation between the two responses is not taken into account. When the same individual makes two judgments, there is always the possibility of correlation. In determining the degree of significance, this possibility must be incorporated into the statistical argument. The only way to correct for this is to account for internal distribution of a table whose marginals comprise the proportions whose difference is being assessed. Thus, we obtain the following table from a sample of employees in a government office. They were asked to judge statements as whether rules in their organization were like the bureaucratic norm and whether the rules ought to be like the bureaucratic norm. The constructions were not this blunt, of course, but in effect this was what they did. The question became Do more employees think the rules are bureaucratic than think they ought to be?

	Is		
	Like a bureaucracy	Not like a bureaucracy	Total
Ought:			
Like a bureaucracy	37	2	39
Not like a bureaucracy	24	33	57
Total	61	35	96

Whatever differences appear in the marginal totals must be attributed to those whose assessment of what is was different from their assessment of what ought to be. Those who maintained their judgment do not affect the marginal differences.

To develop a completely general argument, we will fall back on our paradigm of the two-by-two table. Although we shall use as an example items responded to by the same subjects, a before-and-after argument conforms to the same model. In the table A and $\sim$A refer to responses to one item, C and $\sim$C to responses on the other item.

	A	$\sim$A	t
C	a	b	$n_1.$
$\sim$C	c	d	$n_2.$
t	$n._1$	$n._2$	N

The problem is whether there is any difference between $p = n._1/N$ and $p = n_1./N$. If this had been a before-and-after problem, the question would have been, Has there been any *change* in the marginal proportions, as defined? The modification is verbal. However, one may wish then to modify the symbols accompanying what now appears as C and $\sim$C and have the same categories as are in the "before" dimension.

Categories a and d represent no change, or no differences. The only places where change could occur are in b and c. The following observations are permissible:

1. $b + c =$ the number of individuals who changed.
2. If this number of changers is explainable on the basis of chance, an equal number should have gone in each direction.
3. The expected frequency can be defined as

$$E = \frac{b+c}{2}$$

4. Then the observed frequency would be denoted by either b or c.

For the computation of chi-square,

$$\chi^2 = \Sigma \frac{(O - E)^2}{E}$$

we must determine the difference $(O - E)$. This would result in

$$b - \frac{b+c}{2} = \frac{2b - b - c}{2} = \frac{b-c}{2}$$

(8.4)

In computing χ^2 for cell b, we would have

$$\chi^2_b = \frac{\frac{(b-c)^2}{2}}{\frac{b+c}{2}} = \frac{(b-c)^2}{2^2} \cdot \frac{2}{(b+c)} = \frac{(b-c)^2}{2(b+c)}$$

Were we to compute χ^2 for cell c we would have

$$\frac{(c-b)^2}{2(b+c)}$$

Because $(b-c)^2 = (c-b)^2$ in numerical value, either representation is acceptable. Adding these values together, we obtain

$$\chi^2 = \frac{(b-c)^2}{2(b+c)} + \frac{(b-c)^2}{2(b+c)} + \frac{(b-c)^2}{b+c}$$

(8.5)

This χ^2 has one degree of freedom: since $b+c$ equals the total amount of change, knowledge of either b or c completely determines the others.

Returning to our empirical example, we find

$$\chi^2 = \frac{(24-2)^2}{24+2} = \frac{22^2}{24} = 18.5$$

This is certainly a stronger relation than that given by the erroneous calculation. To determine the amount of association, we must observe that the *most* change that could occur would be in one direction. Hence the maximum amount of change in one direction must equal $b+c$; the amount of change in the other direction would equal zero. If we arbitrarily let b equal $(b+c)$ and c equal 0, 8.5 would give us

$$\chi^2 = \frac{[(b+c)-0]^2}{b+c} = \frac{(b+c)^2}{b+c} = b+c$$

This is the maximum value of chi-square under these conditions. If we define ϕ^2 (as before) as the ratio of an empirically computed χ^2 to its theoretical maximum, we get

$$\phi^2 = \frac{\chi^2}{b+c} = \frac{\dfrac{(b-c)^2}{b+c}}{b+c} = \frac{(b-c)^2}{b+c} \cdot \frac{1}{(b+c)} =$$

$$\frac{(b-c)^2}{(b+c)^2} = \left(\frac{b-c}{b+c}\right)^2$$

(8.6)

and, obviously,

$$\phi = \frac{b-c}{b+c}$$

(8.7)

In our case,

$$\phi^2 = \frac{18.5}{26} = .68$$

and

$$\phi = \frac{22}{26} = .83$$

The erroneously computed chi-square was only about half of the correct one; but the erroneously computed phi-square was about a thirteenth of the one based upon the correctly calculated chi-square.

Clearly, the model one proposes as a limiting case is of crucial interest. Moreover, the inference drawn from 8.5 and 8.6 does not include the ideas of association previously discussed. One may have perfect correlation, either positive or negative, and 8.5 would equal zero. This would be true also in the case of a random relation. In general, 8.5 will tend to approach zero in any symmetrical table. For the weak logical relations (implication, subimplication, contrariety, subcontrariety), however, 8.5 will tend to approach unity.

The two-by-two table in scale construction. The two-by-two table has been used as a model for showing how items in a multi-item test may be related. Recently, its use in discussing the reproducibility coefficient in the Guttman scale has been developed.[3] However, the two-by-two table is fundamental neither to the idea of, nor to the operations central to, the Guttman scale. There are scaling operations, however, which make good use of the two-by-two table.

There are, for example, a number of items in a test—either a theoretical or a practical instrument—from which one wishes to develop a single score. This score is to represent at least a summarization of responses to the items; at best, it is to represent a position along some quantitative dimension. The problems are to choose which items one wishes to retain and assign some weight to each item retained. It is, from a theoretical point of view, possible to retain all items which happen to be proposed. This may be inefficient, however, in that retaining an item which is randomly associated with the dimension to be measured, or the result to be predicted, takes time, and adds nothing to one's knowledge.

Two general procedures have been given for determining the items to be retained. One involves an outside criterion; the other makes use of internal consistency, assuming face validity. Let us imagine that someone wanted to measure success in some type of activity or radicalism in po-

143

litical science. In the first case, one could dichotomize subjects on the basis of success and failure in the specified activity. Naturally, the basis for this judgment must be outside the test—opinion of superiors, income, grade-point average—*something which is theoretically acceptable.* After the selection of the criterion, there ought to be no doubt as to the correctness of the criterion of success. Similarly with radicalism; it is usual to take two groups known to differ with respect to radicalism. One may first assign an arbitrary score of 1 to each correct response; then each respondent would be given as a tentative score the total of the correct responses; these scores would be dichotomized as "high" and "low" at the mean or median. The high scores may represent success, or radicalism, or whatever is being measured, and the low scores whatever alternative seems reasonable. We now have some criterion established. This criterion has but two alternatives.

The response to each item may also be dichotomized. The simplest one would be a correct response (deemed correct by the researcher or a group of judges, or a necessary result of the question—as in a true-false test). Other possibilities are legion. The response may be "favorable" or "unfavorable," with the subjects choosing. Or the responses may be given various degrees of favorableness, which are dichotomized by the researcher. Agree-disagree is another favorite. In any event, each item is dichotomized on the basis of the response.

The procedure for selecting items to be retained is simple. Each item is correlated with the criterion dichotomy. Obviously, this can be done in a two-by-two table. The items which are associated beyond chance are retained. Those items within the range of a chance explanation are removed. It is as simple as that.

The kind of logical relation required between a good test item and the validating criterion is a major issue, not fully resolved. At first glance, it would seem that either if-and-only-if relations or contradictory ones should be presumed ideal. Yet in a research situation the relation may be relatively weak. Putting the criterion groups in the position of antecedents, and the response to the item in the position of the consequent, we may construct the following table:

	Success	Failure
Correct response	a	b
Incorrect response	c	d

The reason for putting the criterion group in the position of antecedent is the assumption that the response to an item is a function of the degree of success. However, if one assumes that agreement with a criterion is a function of correct response—and, ultimately, one is likely to want to use the items to predict membership in the success and failure categories—then the tabular representation would be changed.

Continuing the example based on the assumption that response is a function of success, we need to determine which error is the greater: inferring an incorrect response from membership in a success category, or inferring a correct response from membership in the failure group. If the former error is of little consequence, then b should approach zero. If, however, the latter error is of little consequence, then a should approach zero. If neither error can be tolerated, then the weak relations must be avoided and only strong relations permitted. If a researcher fails to recognize the implications of this decision, he is likely to accept any measure that is reasonably strong. But it could turn out that by mixing the two errors, the strength of a given logical relation would be watered down, and the ultimate utility of the test be weakened. Accordingly, the type of error to be tolerated should be chosen early, and used as a criterion of acceptance.

An obvious idea about weighting follows from the observation that there is a greater or less probability of being wrong when the chance hypothesis is rejected. If the chance of being wrong on a particular item is very small, one ought to give relatively great weight to that item. When an item barely rejects chance, it ought not be given as much weight as the former kind. This suggests that some measure of the degree of correlation can be used to determine the weights assigned to each item.

A sensible weighting system would appear to be one in which the weight increases with an increasing amount of correlation. If any item were uniquely related to the event to be predicted—if necessary and sufficient conditions obtained—only that item would be necessary and it should have infinite weight. Accordingly, a formula for weighting system would be

$$W = \frac{1}{1-r}$$

(8.8)

where r denotes any acceptable correlation ratio. I have discussed a number of them. Certainly tetrachoric r is a suitable one for the situation of correlating a response dichotomy to a tentative score. Phi-square would seem to be another appropriate measure, and is flexible enough to allow for various logical relations. There is probably no argument against any of the various measures which have been proposed, except those offered in the second section of this chapter.

From this point on, the technique may become merely more complicated. One may decide that for any item in the test, the difference between the responses (favorable or unfavorable) should equal unity. Accordingly, a favorable response would be assigned a weight given by 8.8 while an unfavorable response would be given $1 - W$. If the table generating 8.8 is properly arranged, the result will always be a number greater than unity, so that the unfavorable response would be a negative number. Another possibility is to require that the sum of responses to any item must equal zero. This is achieved by assigning a positive weight to the favorable response, and a negative weight of the same magnitude to the unfavorable response. Clearly, this makes best sense for a symmetrical table.

As a matter of strategy, one may seek negatively stated items. The reason for this is obvious. Were they all stated in one way, the respondent might become impressed with this appearance and take a chance on subscribing to all items. If the responses involve positive and negative directions, the algebraic sign attached to the correlation coefficient must be maintained. Then the person taking the affirmative answer would be given a negative weight, while the person who took the negative answer would be given a positive one. But this is a matter of the strategy of testing and measurement.

The problem of joint effects.[4] Let it be assumed that some type of causal analysis has proceeded, using the two-by-two tables suggested in this volume. Let it further be assumed that chance has been rejected and that some logical relation can be asserted. For the moment, which relation is of no interest. Let it be denoted as R_1.

Regardless of the magnitude of any measure of association (or cause), the stability of the relationship may be doubted. A better formulation, perhaps, is this: Does the relation R_1 hold generally, or do the terms have a different relation (R_2) under other circumstances? Thus, we may find that social problems and enacted law may have R_1 relation under certain conditions. If these conditions are altered, does the same relation

146

exist, or does the relation change? If the relationship changes, joint effects are said to exist.[5]

The problem may be shown in the following contingency table. I use a new system of symbols to denote cell frequencies. I do this for two reasons: the multiple-subscript system will enable those who wish to relate this presentation to the table in Chapter 2 to do so more easily; and we will find use for the letters a and b in certain equations. Perhaps the reader should be warned: the arithmetic involved in the test for joint effects is very complex. In the table, F_2 and $\sim F_2$ are secondary control factors, F_1 and $\sim F_1$ are primary conditions or factors, and C and $\sim C$ are consequents. No notation will be given for any of the marginals. These can readily be determined from various combinations of cell frequencies as the occasion demands.

	F_2		$\sim F_2$	
	F_1	$\sim F_1$	F_1	$\sim F_1$
C	n_{111}	n_{112}	n_{121}	n_{122}
$\sim C$	n_{211}	n_{212}	n_{221}	n_{222}

If F_1 and C stand in a particular logical relation, in general, the introduction of the secondary controls ought to make no difference. Accordingly, F_1 and C ought to have the same kind of relationship under F_2 as under $\sim F_2$. If the relationship changes, we have joint effects. To illustrate the issue, we may have a strong implicatory relation under F_2 and independence or contradiction under $\sim F_2$. Clearly, this possibility ought to be tested.

Let the cell proportions be determined by dividing the cell frequency by the total N. Then it can be shown that a condition of no joint effects will be true if the following relation obtains:

$$\frac{p_{111}\, p_{221}}{p_{211}\, p_{121}} = \frac{p_{112}\, p_{222}}{p_{212}\, p_{122}}$$

$$(8.9)$$

In general, this will not be true. Indeed, even in the absence of joint effects, 6.11 will not be precisely true. To determine whether or not 6.11 is sufficiently near a relation of equality to permit the inference of a mere chance deviation, it is necessary to introduce a term in the definitions of p_{ijk}. This term must have the characteristic of permitting the mathe-

147

matician to put some limiting condition upon its effect in a subsequent equation. This term is the Lagrange multiplier.[6] The use of this gimmick will become apparent later on.

The terms are inserted in the following manner: in computing the p_{ijk}'s under the assumption of no joint effects, the multiplier is added to the cell frequencies of the terms comprising the major diagonal of F_2 and the minor diagonal of $\sim F_2$; it is subtracted from the other cell frequencies. Then 6.11 can be written

$$\frac{(n_{111} + \lambda)(n_{221} + \lambda)}{(n_{211} - \lambda)(n_{121} - \lambda)} = \frac{(n_{112} - \lambda)(n_{222} - \lambda)}{(n_{212} + \lambda)(n_{122} + \lambda)}$$

(8.10)

If we complete the multiplications indicated, and insert convenient terms to be shorthand equivalents for longer arithmetic procedures, 8.10 becomes

$$\frac{\lambda + a_1 \lambda + b_1}{\lambda - a_2 \lambda + b_2} = \frac{\lambda - a_3 \lambda + b_3}{\lambda + a_4 \lambda + b_4}$$

(8.11)

This may not seem like much of an advance. But it is indeed. For we can solve 8.11 for λ in a relatively easy manner.

In solving for λ, we may impose the condition cited earlier. This we do now. We find that 8.11 generates the following cubic:

$$A_0\lambda^3 + A_1\lambda^2 + A_2\lambda + A_3 = 0$$

(8.12)

Before showing where the A_i's come from, I present a ready-made solution to 8.12. One thing the reader who is not well acquainted with mathematics should understand is that the mathematician is probably not the genius the nonmathematician suspects he is; for most mathematicians are unable to keep long equations in their heads the way geniuses do. What the mathematician often does is to substitute short symbols for longer ones. This lessens the task for the time being. All that he has to do is to remember to put the longer terms back into the equation later on. This explains part of the mystery of mathematics. Those new terms are simply shorthand ways of saying something complicated.

The first step in solving 8.12 involves a simple kind of transformation. Remember, the idea is to make 8.12 less complicated than it now is. The easiest way to do that is to make the coefficient of λ vanish. The best way to do that is to divide all terms in 8.12 by that number. Nothing happens to zero when it is divided by A_0; but A_0 divided by itself equals unity and need never appear in the equation. Rather than carry fractions around, we may substitute symbols that stand for fractions. This we do, and 8.12 becomes

$$\lambda^3 = b\lambda + c\lambda + d = 0 \tag{8.13}$$

where the symbols standing for the fractions are

$$b = \frac{A_1}{A_0}$$

$$c = \frac{A_2}{A_0}$$

$$d = \frac{A_3}{A_0}$$

This step is simply a gimmick to make the arithmetic solution easier. Like the following substitution, nothing is added or taken away. The reason we make the next substitution is to get 8.13 in a form that is already solved. In fact, the next equation, 8.14, is solved in most texts in college algebra.[7] Hence, we make the following substitutions (remember that sometimes we have to put them back):

Invent the following relations:

$$\lambda = \theta - \frac{b}{3}$$

$$C = c - \frac{b^2}{3}$$

$$D = d - \frac{bc}{3} + \frac{2b^3}{27}$$

insert them into 8.13.

$$\theta^3 + C\theta + D = 0 \tag{8.14}$$

One bit of magic remains. We must introduce two unknowns into 8.14 whose sum will equal a root of 8.14. The reason for this substitution is to enable us to impose the condition that these two unknowns will have a functional relation equaling zero. Had we substituted one unknown, we would have been no further along toward a solution than before.

149

Obviously θ is a root of 8.14. We said that the two unknowns (call them U and V) must equal a root of 8.14. Hence we say

$$\theta = U + V$$

Now we impose this restriction on U and V:

$$3\,UV + C = 0 \tag{8.15}$$

Upon substitution, we find that 8.14 reduces to

$$U^3 + V^3 + D = 0 \tag{8.16}$$

One solution of 8.16 is virtually immediate:

$$U^3 = \frac{-D}{2} \pm \frac{1}{2}\sqrt{D^2 + \frac{4C^3}{27}}$$

$$\tag{8.17.1}$$

Now, U and V were symmetrically introduced into the solution of our equation, so we may arbitrarily select one to represent the solution with a plus sign before the radical; the other will have a negative sign. Thus

$$U^3 = \frac{-D}{2} + \frac{1}{2}\sqrt{D^2 + \frac{4C^3}{27}}$$

$$\tag{8.17.2}$$

$$V^3 = \frac{-D}{2} - \frac{1}{2}\sqrt{D^2 + \frac{4C^3}{27}}$$

$$\tag{8.17.3}$$

All of the data in the right-hand members of 8.17.2 and 8.17.3 come from empirical data; only an arithmetic solution will remain. The use of logs will make the determination of the cube roots of U and V a bit easier.[8]

Remembering our series of substitutions, we must work our way back to original data. The first step is to determine lambda:

$$\lambda = U + V - \frac{A_1}{3A_0} \tag{8.18}$$

The A_i terms in 8.12 and subsequent formulae are found by the following relations.

$$A_0 = a_1 + a_2 + a_3 + a_4 = N \tag{8.19.1}$$

$$A_1 = (a_1 a_4 + b_1 + b_4) - (a_2 a_3 + b_2 + b_3) \tag{8.19.2}$$

$$A_2 = a_1b_4 + a_2b_3 + a_3b_2 + a_4b_1 \qquad (8.19.3)$$

$$A_3 = b_1b_4 - b_2b_3 \qquad (8.19.4)$$

where the lower-case letters are obtained from cell frequencies in the following way:

$$a_1 = n_{111} + n_{221} \qquad (8.20.1)$$
$$a_2 = n_{211} + n_{121} \qquad (8.20.2)$$
$$a_3 = n_{112} + n_{222} \qquad (8.20.3)$$
$$a_4 = n_{212} + n_{122} \qquad (8.20.4)$$
$$b_1 = (n_{111})(n_{221}) \qquad (8.20.5)$$
$$b_2 = (n_{211})(n_{121}) \qquad (8.20.6)$$
$$b_3 = (n_{112})(n_{222}) \qquad (8.20.7)$$
$$b_4 = (n_{212})(n_{122}) \qquad (8.20.8)$$

Before proceeding to an illustration of the arithmetic, we must take note of some ideas about no joint effects and how that is related to a lambda in the neighborhood of zero. Consider the table:

	F_2		$\sim F_2$	
	F_1	$\sim F_1$	F_1	$\sim F_1$
C	n_{111}	n_{112}	n_{121}	n_{122}
$\sim C$	n_{211}	n_{212}	n_{221}	n_{222}

Recall equation 8.12:

$$A_0\lambda^3 + A_1\lambda^2 + A_2\lambda + A_3 = 0$$

Note that whenever A_3 equals zero, lambda must also equal zero. The reason is that (at least) A_0 never equals zero since it equals N. Unless lambda equals zero, 8.12 cannot be true. Accordingly, we must observe the conditions under which A_3 equals zero. We see from 8.19.4 that this situation exists when $b_1b_4 - b_2b_3$ equals zero. This can occur when the two products are equal: when randomness exists on both sides of the table. From the 8.20 series of equations, we observe that whenever the logical relation under F_2 appears under $\sim F_2$, then 8.19.4 will equal zero and, by implication, so will lambda. When lambda equals zero, we are unable to infer the presence of joint effects. Whenever lambda is significantly different from zero, we may infer joint effects.

The following chi-square, with one degree of freedom, enables one to test the premise that lambda equals zero. It is to be observed that whenever lambda is less than unity (actually, when it is less than 3.841) chi-square cannot be significant. Hence, there is no need to compute the statistic under such conditions. The equation follows:

$$\chi^2 = \frac{\lambda^2}{n} \sum_i \sum_j \sum_k P_{ijk}{}^{-1}$$

or

$$\chi^2 = \lambda^2 \left[\frac{1}{n_{111} + \lambda} + \frac{1}{n_{221} + \lambda} + \frac{1}{n_{212} + \lambda} + \frac{1}{n_{122} + \lambda} \right.$$

$$\left. + \frac{1}{n_{112} - \lambda} + \frac{1}{n_{222} - \lambda} + \frac{1}{n_{211} - \lambda} + \frac{1}{n_{121} - \lambda} \right] \tag{8.22}$$

Clearly, the test for joint effects entails a considerable amount of effort. It is not likely to become a popular statistical argument. Yet if one wishes to precisely test the hypothesis of joint effects, a test of this sort is required for the two-by-two table. I illustrate the computations with an example drawn from contemporary research.

In the research cited previously regarding attitudes of a class of rural Minnesota high school seniors, one question concerned their recent consideration of the possibility of migrating. Because of the known fact that farm females have tended to migrate in greater proportions than farm males, the relation between sex and a tendency to answer affirmatively the question, "Have you recently seriously thought of moving from this area?" was sought. One set of high schools, it will be recalled, was in an area economically dependent largely upon mining. Another set of schools was in an area where agriculture and resorts were the main industries. Because of the difference in opportunity in the two types of economy, it seemed possible that the tendency to have thought about moving could change from one area to the other. In particular, the hypothesis that serious consideration of likely migration was sex-related *independently* of area could be developed. The following analysis tests the premise of in-

Table 3. High School Seniors' Answers to the Question: "Have You Thought Seriously of Moving?", Classified by Sex

Answer	Farming and Resort		Mining	
	Male	Female	Male	Female
Yes	$n_{111} = 121$	$n_{112} = 151$	$n_{121} = 138$	$n_{122} = 107$
No	$n_{211} = 142$	$n_{212} = 170$	$n_{221} = 120$	$n_{222} = 92$

dependence; the relation to sex is not of interest at the moment. The data are shown in Table 3.

Utilizing the 8.20 series of equations, we see that

$$a_1 = 121 + 120 = 241 \qquad b_1 = (121)(120) = 14,520$$
$$a_2 = 142 + 138 = 280 \qquad b_2 = (142)(138) = 19,596$$
$$a_3 = 151 + \ 92 = 243 \qquad b_3 = (151)(92) \ = 13,892$$
$$a_4 = 170 + 107 = 277 \qquad b_4 = (170)(107) = 18,190$$

Then inserting these approximately in the 8.19 series, we obtain

$$A_0 = 241 + 280 + 243 + 277 = 1,041$$
$$A_1 = [66,757 + 14,520 + 18,190] - [68,040 + 19,596 + 13,892] = -2,061$$
$$A_2 = 17,057,418$$
$$A_3 = -8,108,832$$

Substituting in 8.12,

$$1,041\lambda^3 - 2,061\lambda^2 + 17,057,418\lambda - 8,108,832 = 0$$

and 8.13 becomes

$$\lambda^3 - 1.98\lambda^2 + 16,385\lambda - 7,789.4 = 0$$

Since

$$C = 16,385 - \frac{(-1.98)^2}{3} + 16,383.69$$

and

$$D = -7,789.4 - \frac{(-1.98)(16,385)}{3} + \frac{2(1.98)^3}{27} = 3,027.13$$

8.17.2 becomes

$$\theta^3 + 16,383.96\,\theta + 3,024.3 = 0$$
$$U^3 = \frac{-3,024.13}{2} + \frac{1}{2}\sqrt{(-3,024.13)^2 + \frac{(4)(16,383.69)^3}{27}}$$
$$U = 73.81$$

Accordingly,

$$V = -73.95$$
$$\lambda = 73.81 - 73.95 - \left(\frac{-1.98}{3}\right)$$

Hence, lambda is found to be equal to .52 (approximately). Since this is much smaller than unity, it cannot possibly be significant. We see no need to compute chi-square in this case. The inference which seems to be warranted is that there is no evidence for believing that the relation between sex and recent thought of moving changes from one area to the other. No joint effects exist in this set of data.

CHAPTER 9

Summary and Conclusions

THE problem proposed by methodologists is to develop rules which will permit the inferences necessary to the development of a scientific theory. A discussion of probability led to the conclusion that probability is a primitive idea. Every attempt at definition contained some reference to an idea similar in meaning to probability. Even the vapid notion that probability is a measure of the some-ness of particular propositions contains a tautology. Similarly, cause appears to be a primitive concept for the simple reason that science cannot imagine anything uncaused. Its use may be the result of asking Why?[1]

Some writers seem to hold probability and causation as essentially contradictory concepts. Most proposed measures of association, or whatever the term may be, presuppose a limit of absolute certainty: when causes are unknown, the argument holds, probabilities are not needed. Similar to this argument is the position that asserts that probability is a measure of ignorance: when we have real knowledge, we will have no need for probability.

To me, this contention is an error. For one thing, I posit the principle of necessary error in measurement. Hence, no certain propositions are ever possible. Probability assertions will always be required when the content has a this-worldly referent. This means that no one can ever devise a test to determine whether probabilities inhere in the world or result from error in our measures. It is not the task of statistics to determine whether or not the world is causally or casually put together. For the other thing, as we saw, the notion of uncause seems impossible to accept. It is without meaning. One can hardly claim that probability is also without meaning.

The difficulty lies in the fact that cause is not a thing to be observed. The idea of cause is related to explanation. An assertion of mere association does not constitute an explanation: until the relationship is *required* by theory, no explanation exists. Until a structural connection is shown necessitating the inference of association, no explanation exists. Now, an explanation is related to the assertion of relations. When a relation exists such that an appeal to the principle of relation requires an inference of the empirical association, then an explanation does exist. Clearly, cause may be regarded as a particular kind of principle of relation. What is required is a set of rules which permit the conclusion that this kind of relation does exist.

This kind of proof proceeds exactly as does any proof. One deduces the consequents of the truth of an asserted causal relation. Then one does research to determine whether or not these consequences appear in fact. Falsification of the consequent permits a rejection of the proposed cause. But the verification of the consequent does not prove the proposed cause. Empirically, one never has final, certain proof. The truth of the proposed cause cannot be rejected, and hence is accepted. The reason for accepting the proposed cause as true exists in the a priori theoretical necessity of proposing the causal relation. Although probability was not *defined*, we have seen that various proposed definitions were actually *measures* of probability. The equally likely case was noted as a special case of probability. In particular, however, the Tchebycheff Inequality led to an important principle. If there is a parametric value of probability, it is possible to estimate this with any stated degree of accuracy less than certainty. The principle is usually called the law of large numbers and warrants faith in probability estimates of universe values—if such values exist.

The problem of relationships evokes the image of logic. Among other matters, we have the issue of the formal relation of propositions. The statement-form "All S are P" is not a proposition. It is simply the form of a proposition. When the terms S and P are defined, the sentence conveys some information. Note, however, that *all* and *are* are undefined. It should not be imagined that some terms are peculiarly subjects and others peculiarly predicates. If the statement "All *S* are *P*" is true, the same information may be conveyed in other forms. Thus, one may say, "The class *S*-and-not-*P* has no members," or "Some of the *P* is all of the *S*" and convey the same information as before. Thus we must agree that the terms subject and predicate are merely parts of a traditional grammar, and have no necessary correspondence with the real world.

Theory, however, may compel a specific relation between subject and predicate terms. This is especially true when the terms relate to antecedents and consequents. If one cannot in theory distinguish between them, one may sensibly speak of association. At the same time we must note that what appears as an antecedent in one problem may appear as a consequent in another.

Logical relations could be assessed through the use of a two-by-two table. It was apparent that different ideas of causal relations were closely connected with various logical relations. The logical relation, as conveyed by a two-by-two table, was proposed as a model. An example was given in which the table generated four types. Then it was necessary to appeal to theory to determine the possible existence of each type. Subsequent to the verification of their theoretical possibility, an appeal to knowledge was necessary to estimate the relative likelihood of a given type's actually occurring. From this estimation a particular logical relation could be offered as a model, completely analogous to the mathematical model so dear to the hearts of our younger contemporaries.

Various measures were proposed to indicate the extent to which some model alternative to chance was approximated. This will be summarized in the next section.

Of more immediate consequence is the observation that all research is done in a social situation. I do not allude merely to the common culture shared by most scientists. Nor do I refer alone to the social life that scientists engage in outside their professional activity. I refer to the social background of any learning experience; I refer to the social history of any symbol.

I cannot tolerate a methodology based on the assumption that the scientist is an inert object. I do not believe that the human mind needs only to be properly hit with stimuli to achieve a scientifically complex theory of the world. Man, the scientist, is an active creature. He is not passively related to the world. The world does not come to him: he goes to the world. He recreates *parts* of the world, in the laboratory, for example, to test out ideas. The true scientist is a creative being. No machine he: no rules tell him what premises to consider; rules tell him which, of all premises, are worthy of retention. Furthermore, man invents these rules. They are not thrust upon him.

No scientist today is able to perform all the tasks necessary for a scientific study. He must employ others to act for him. He must train these technicians to do his bidding, just as he must create machines to perform routine tasks (as in computations). A "creative" lackey might spoil the broth, so the scientist may develop rules to govern the behavior of these technically competent substitutes. It happens that in many fields of inquiry, the technician is an apprentice scientist. Many graduate students, for example, first do a stint of lab work. There, they must learn the technician's role. This will prove helpful later when they direct the activities of such workers. But it should never be imagined that learning how to be a competent helper is the same as learning how to be a scientist. It is true that the apprentice learns much from the master. But no master would ever dream of governing his own behavior with the rules he imposes upon the apprentice. This is because the master is allowed to think. The apprentice, until he masters the tricks of the trade, cannot control his material sufficiently to make an idea become a reality. Analogously, the scientist decides what premises are to be considered, what rules are proper, what constitutes a proof. The technician merely does as he is told—or at least he should.

Time passes during a research activity, whereas logical relations, like mathematical relations, are instantaneous. Hence methodology cannot be considered merely logic. In connection with this we faced the issue of induction. I could not accept the idea of an inductive logic. Nor could I happily accept the doctrine that induction stands for a set of rules to guide in discovering new ideas. This messy way of thinking is a necessary adjunct of the notion that a scientist is passively oriented to the world. What it neglects is the passage of time; for passage of time suggests that induction refers properly to the process of research.

The fundamental difficulty lies in the inability of some people to properly locate the segment of doubt in a research activity. It is commonplace to call the scientific attitude one characterized by doubt. Since Descartes said "Cogito ergo sum," scientists have been doubting.[2] But little attention is paid to what is doubted. At one time or another, everything is doubted. Some doubt is resolved by faith: by accepting some idea as primitively true. Some doubt is resolved by research design. Let us imagine that a scientist has endeavored to make an assertion of the form "If P, then Q." Many things can be doubted about this statement: the correctness of the premise, the conclusion, the relation itself. The last doubt is characteristic of the sophisticated sciences.

Doubt may be associated with various phases of the scientific process. In general, we can note three fundamentally different areas of doubt; each area corresponds to a different kind of research activity. As the reader will note, considerable activity has been engaged in mistakenly. Some writers have confused the various kinds of activity, feeling that what is true for one kind must be true for all. The naïveté of such a confusion will become readily apparent. The three kinds of activity I call inquiry, research, and analysis.[3]

Inquiry. Both theory and the world of facts are doubted in inquiry. Indeed, not much about either is known in this kind of research. If, instead of having precisely-stated hypotheses, one simply has some questions he wants answered, he is engaged in inquiry. The notion, occasionally offered in this connection, of having an implicit hypothesis is of small value. "Implicit hypothesis" is a contradiction in terms. A hypothesis is a statement of relations proposed to be tested; as such it must be explicitly stated. If it is implicit it cannot be properly tested: its explication is an *ad hoc* assertion, and, as such, must be submitted anew for test.

For a long time, methodologists have been busily formulating ways of testing hypotheses. They have seldom discussed how to develop hypotheses. It is as if developing hypotheses were nonscientific and only testing hypotheses were scientific. This is a crude notion. It is like the old idea that only mathematically defined functional relations constitute scientific propositions. It forgives the scientist for any inability to think. It allows for an "idiotic" scientist, who can only tend machines. The belief that the scientist is creative, on the other hand, allows for inquiry as a process in developing hypotheses. Clearly, induction as a process is consistent with the idea of admitting inquiry as a form of scientific activity.

It must be understood that inquiry is incapable of offering proof. It may, however, be very convincing.

Research. In research, it is not so much the world of fact that is doubted as the asserted relations. Early stages of science may be called inquiry. The *ad hoc* solution of a problem becomes a proposed hypothesis. In research, the scientist must (a) attempt to recreate the conditions asserted in the *ad hoc* solution; (b) replicate the operations of data-gathering and data-assessing; and (c) determine whether or not the relation between the subject and predicate terms recurs sufficiently often to constitute an explanation. Clearly, most technical discussions of science fall under the rubric of research—the derivation is obvious—*re-search*.

When the hypothesis offered as a result of inquiry fails, the scientist must make a decision. He must either draw a line and assert his conclusions, or he must attempt to develop a new hypothesis to account for his data. If he has a technician's view of research, he will merely assert that the hypothesis has failed. But if he has a creative attitude toward his work, he will attempt to develop an argument sufficient to account for his data. He knows that this, too, is an *ad hoc* argument. But he knows that this is one way to get hypotheses. He knows that it may later be tested.

Parenthetically, I offer a comment to graduate students in pursuit of their doctoral degrees. Ordinarily, the doctoral dissertation for a research degree is required to contain "an original contribution to knowledge." At the same time, the student is expected to execute a design that permits a rigorous test of hypotheses. Now, we have seen that originality inheres in inquiry and rigorous tests inhere in research. The student is somehow expected to engage in both inquiry and research in the same process. No wonder he feels a certain amount of discouragement and frustration!

One way out is to attempt to reconstruct existing theory in such a way that one may deduce a hypothesis from the acceptable content. So far, we have not mentioned such a source of ideas. At any rate, such a source of ideas can be acceptable only if theory is recognized as being prior to data. One difficulty with this business of deducing hypotheses is that it is much easier to develop hypotheses consistent with theory than ones which are required by theory. Perhaps the former is sufficient; it is, however, not very convincing. That may be the reason why this source of hypotheses has not been much used in the social sciences.

Analysis. When theoretical relations are not doubted, but only the world of fact, we have analysis. Appealing to a technique of information-gathering (as in a survey or census), analysis accepts theory as being true in order to permit an interpretation of the data. Thus one may survey a city to determine the status of housing. Then, believing a theory that relates housing to delinquency, one can interpret the data to point out danger spots, and so on.

Clearly, analysis is geared to practical activity; first, because no doubt is permitted, and hence no test is included or possible; second, because it is fastened to a unique historical situation. The survey is concerned with the here and now. The data are analyzed for immediate use. Just as a chemist assesses a solution in terms of contemporary theory, so may a sociologist interpret a study of attitudes.

Most social scientists proudly proclaim their ethical neutrality. If theoretical research is to have practical utility, and if the utilization of science involves an ethical stand, the matter of analysis should demand some attention, from both an ethical and a theoretical point of view. It is interesting to observe the behavior of social scientists who see physicists, engineers, and other technical scientists being asked their opinions on social questions while social scientists look on. Were the social scientists willing to show how their theories are related to practical affairs, perhaps they would replace the nonexperts in the halls of government.

If man is to bring the past into his preparations for the future, then clearly analysis must be more fully developed than it has been. An important issue must be squarely met. If the theory is based upon an empiricism containing only process time, and analysis is wedded to historical time, some change in the substantive argument may be required. The kind of parameter estimated by the research activity may be altogether different from the kind of parameter interested in analysis. Yet there can be no doubt: in the matter of practical consequences, more attention must be paid to the kind of activity that I have been calling analysis.

Consider, for example, the kind of difficulty which generates an interest in analysis. We noted the location in space and time of the problems proposed for analysis. But more important, perhaps, is the social position of the person who becomes interested in the problem. For example, it may turn out that traffic fatalities are the result of a culturally defined competitive complex that all members of the male world are absorbed in winning. This spirit of competition may result in a large number of traffic accidents. The question that must be answered is this: Who can control the variables contained in the theoretical argument? The fact remains that much interest in practical affairs is manifested in individual, not group, behavior. Thus, analysis may reveal that the application of a theory containing variables whose manipulation is possible only by cultural entities (rather than by any particular subculture or individual) is deficient.

It is, perhaps, curious that few positivists who proclaim their students, if not themselves, as the new priests, have interested themselves in variables which the individual can manipulate. Most philosophers of that school have become enamored of the big things—like institutions—which cannot be manipulated by any one person. Historically, it has been the anti-positivist theorist in the social sciences who has championed the assessment of variables manipulatable by individual persons. Not that the anti-positivist has neglected culture or such things; but he has tried to develop types of action which the positivist has found abhorrent. Be that as it may, those scientists who proclaim that the goal of science is prediction, who wed research to this world at least in goals, are properly interested in analysis.

Considerable confusion could be avoided if various philosophers of science would say what kind of activity they were discussing. It seems clear that analysis does not describe the activity of inquiry or research; and the latter two are not identical in purpose, scope, or rules. Social scientists have tended to specialize in one or another type of activity. It may be gratifying to proclaim one's special area as being truly scientific while the others are not. But it is, nonetheless, incorrect.

A SUMMARY OF THE TECHNICAL CONTENT

The technical material centered on an analysis of the two-by-two table. The model table for the symbols used is this:

	A	$\sim A$	t
C	a	b	n_1.
$\sim C$	c	d	n_2.
t	$n_{.1}$	$n_{.2}$	N

Since relations between propositions can be logically assessed by means of the two-by-two table, it was proposed that various logical relations could be used as theoretical models in research.

Strong relations exist when one of the diagonals contains a zero. That is, if a and d or b and c are zero, a strong relation exists.

162

SUMMARY AND CONCLUSIONS

Weak relations exist when a zero appears in only one cell. Implicatory relations exist when a zero appears in one cell (b or c) of the minor diagonal, and contrary relations when a zero appears in one cell of the major diagonal. Because of the principle of imperfect measurement, however, a zero is not required. All that is required is that one or more cells approach zero.

Necessary and sufficient conditions. Causal analysis going beyond mere association has become popular as a quest for necessary and sufficient conditions, as though the word "condition" avoids the difficulties inherent in the assemblage and ordering of letters spelling "cause." Sufficient conditions

	A	~A
C		
~C	0	

are obviously related to the idea of implication, whereas necessary conditions

	A	~A
C		0
~C		

are clearly related to the idea of subimplication. The joint occurrence of these conditions evokes the image of a *strong* implicatory relation (if-and-only-if).

Exact probability. From an elementary idea of probability and a rule for combinations of subsets, the exact probability of obtaining any distribution in a two-by-two table was developed. For any given internal distribution,

$$P = \frac{(n_1.!n_2.!n_{.1}!n_{.2}!)}{N!(a!b!c!d!)}$$

To obtain the probability of a given distribution or a more extreme one, the probability of the given table and all subsequent tables obtained by sequential reduction of the smallest cell by unity (keeping the marginal totals) had to be computed and summed.

Chi-square. If the sample size is large—or, rather, if the smallest observed frequency has any magnitude at all—the exact probability test becomes too laborious for use. Accordingly, the chi-square test of independence was offered as a substitute. The traditional equation

$$\chi^2 = \Sigma \frac{(O - E)^2}{E}$$

was shown to be identical with the shortcut method:

$$\chi^2 = \frac{(ad - bc)^2 N}{n_1 . n_2 . n_{.1} n_{.2}}$$

It was later noted that this was equivalent to the square of a critical ratio of proportions.

A correction of the shortcut equation (based on Yates' Correction, and appropriate in the event of small samples) is

$$\chi^2 = \frac{\left[(ad - bc) - \dfrac{N}{2}\right]^2 N}{n_1 . n_2 . n_{.1} n_{.2}}$$

The above equations do not account for correlation. And some degree of correlation is present in a before-and-after test of the same individuals, or when individuals answer the same items. A chi-square appropriate for that situation was found to be

$$\chi^2 = \frac{(b - c)^2}{b + c}$$

Measures of association. Before any logical model can be asserted to have existence, it must be shown that the relation of independence is insufficient to account for the data. Having rejected chance, we desire some measure of the extent of achieving a perfect association.

Phi-square was defined as a ratio of an empirical chi-square to its maximum. The maximum varies according to the model proposed. In any event, this measure is a true percentage: it is the percentage of a maximum chi-square achieved in a given analysis. For strong relations, phi-square is

$$\phi^2 = \frac{\chi^2}{N}$$

For a weak relation, the above formula must be corrected. In general, the formula is obtained by dividing $(ad - bc)^2$ by the product of the column and row totals which share the cell that approaches zero. When correlation must be taken into account, phi-square is found by

$$\phi^2 = \left(\frac{b-c}{b+c}\right)^2$$

Kappa-prime, developed by McCormick in an attempt to measure causal efficiency, involves a new definition of chance. Whereas phi-square appeals to both row and column totals, kappa-prime is independent of row totals. It is also independent of column totals, though its derivation begins with some appeal to the column total. It roughly shows how close a set of data is to perfect causality.

$$\kappa' = \frac{a}{n_{.1}} - \frac{b}{n_{.2}} = p_1 - p_2$$

Tetrachoric r is Pearsonian r's closest relative. It is based on assumptions of normal distributions of linearly related continuous data. As such it may be interpreted as the square root of the percentage of variance explained. One dimension, at least, is a quantitatively defined measure which is reduced to a dichotomy. A formula is

$$r_t = \frac{1}{ij}\left[1 - \frac{1}{N}\sqrt{N^2 - \frac{2ij(bc-ad)}{IJ}}\right]$$

Because of the difficulty of arithmetic computation, a book of diagrams is generally resorted to. In most cases, the error introduced by this method will not alter the conclusions.

D—a rather simple measure—shows the percentage of the amount by which the observed frequency may differ from a chance one in the data at hand.

$$D = 1 - \frac{s}{_s f_t}$$

For a symmetrical table, an average of the D's for separate columns could be computed. This average may be a simple, unweighted, arithmetic average; or it could be a geometric average found by extracting the square root of the product of the column D's.

Lambda, a measure of predictive efficiency, shows the percentage of improvement in guessing an outcome, given the additional information of membership in the antecedent categories.

$$\lambda = \frac{\Sigma P_{am}P_{.m}}{1 - P_{.m}}$$

P—for prediction, apparently—is a very simple-minded assessment. It shows the percentage of the total sample falling in the major diagonal— or minor diagonal, if that should be wanted. In one sense, it shows the percentage of correct prediction, whatever that may mean.

$$P = \frac{a + d}{N}$$

Yule's Q is an undisciplined measure. It approaches unity whenever any logical relation other than independence is achieved. Q measures how close some cell has come to zero, but its interpretation is difficult.

$$Q = \frac{ad - bc}{ad + bc}$$

Coefficient of contingency, when uncorrected, does not even equal unity in its limit. An ordinary correction approaches unity only when the table is symmetrical. By the time it is corrected, an enormous amount of effort has been expended. And the researcher still does not know what it means. This is probably the clumsiest correlation discussed.

$$C = \sqrt{\frac{\chi^2}{\chi^2 + N}}$$

f. *The problem of joint effects.* This proposes a test of joint effects in a two-by-two table of the following form:

	F_2		$\sim F_2$	
	F_1	$\sim F_1$	F_1	$\sim F_1$
C	n_{111}	n_{112}	n_{121}	n_{122}
$\sim C$	n_{211}	n_{212}	n_{221}	n_{222}

If there is a relation between F_1 and C, does that relation hold generally, or does it differ for secondary conditions F_2 and $\sim F_2$? To solve this, the cell proportions (cell frequencies divided by the total n) are modified by Lagrange multipliers. These modifiers generate the equation

$$A_0\lambda^3 + A_1\lambda^2 + A_2\lambda + A_3 = 0$$

where the A_i could be decomposed into the data contained in the table. By an intricate system of substitution, an equation

$$\theta^3 = C\theta + D = 0$$

SUMMARY AND CONCLUSIONS

was developed. The solution for this involves:

$$U^3 = -\frac{D}{2} + \frac{1}{2}\sqrt{D^2 + \frac{4C^3}{27}}$$

$$V^3 = -\frac{D}{2} - \frac{1}{2}\sqrt{D^2 + \frac{4C^3}{27}}$$

Then

$$\lambda = U + V - \frac{A_1}{3A_0}$$

The C and D terms are composed of the A_i terms and are, therefore, available in the data.

A nonchance chi-square implies that $\lambda > 0$. This, in turn, implies that F_1 and C are related differently for F_2 and $\sim F_2$.

Although the arithmetic is formidable, the logic is unassailable. The problem is fairly common; and no number of separate two-by-two tables can answer the question which this lambda proposes to answer. A nonsignificant lambda is required before a particular relation between two propositions can be said to be general.

SOME FINAL CRITICAL COMMENTS

We began our discussion of the two-by-two table by noting that, from an awareness of his past, man seeks to plan for the future. At least some of his plans rest on what we can call scientific knowledge. We must now pay some brief attention to the problem, What good is scientific knowledge? Before we leap too hastily to its defense, allow the critic to have his say.

The parameters assessed in the scientific research may or may not be the same as those in everyday life. In other words, the research activity may center on process time; invariably, the future for which one obtains scientific information is caught in historical time. Analysis, evidently, must get considerable attention if science is to be used by man. This is supported by the observation that the variables discussed by science may not be manipulatable (1) by anyone at all or (2) by a particular person. Simple scientific knowledge, by itself, has no utility. The translation of knowledge into something useful requires some distinct effort.

Cause can never be proved. Indeed, nothing could be directly proved. Even negations, usually regarded as final proofs, are not proved in the

167

sense of finality. The inability to accept A as a cause of C does not warrant the inference that C is uncaused. Our theory may be in error. Although we desire correct theory, we must always be willing to acknowledge the possibility of error. It is not so much that science abhors error as it is that science abhors uncorrected error. Thus, in respect to a proposed A, C may be randomly distributed. If these probabilities obey some laws (i.e., are such that inferences regarding their distribution are warranted), it is entirely possible to recreate the world on the basis of knowledge of this sort. It should be particularly noted that random essentially means obeying the laws of probability: it is a particular kind of order.

Are these probabilities proved? And, of special interest, can it be said that a mathematical derivation proves that a limit exists in the realm of probabilities? Alas, the answer is, as in the case of cause, negative. In a fundamental way, no proof has been given. The taking of samples requires in fact the passage of time. Only if the world does not change during the time that is necessary for taking a sample, and only if the limit existed prior to the taking of the sample, can we sensibly talk about having a limit.

Yet, as every schoolboy knows, highly improbable sequences have some probability of occurring. One may expect an infinite sequence of (say) failures. A sample taken during the sequence of failures may lead to an inference of a high probability of failures. This situation contains a play on words. For one thing, the infinite sequence just mentioned is of a different magnitude than infinite sample. Some ambiguity is present. Of more importance, however, is the unlikelihood of any long run of failures. No probability statement is made with certainty; an estimation of the likelihood of the event is always attached to the statement. In the example in question, we have a problem in run theory, a rather well known area of inquiry.

At the same time, it must be admitted that an appeal to a pragmatic solution—i.e., that experience shows that something of a limit exists—is hardly a proof. Just because the researcher is satisfied that a limit exists—that he is convinced of it—is no proof. But we have reason to believe that if a limit does exist, it can be trapped within very small limits by an increasingly large sample. Failure to find experience corresponding to the inferences flowing from a postulated limit requires a falsification of the limit. While experiences consistent with those inferences do not *require* the acceptance of the proposed limit, they do lend support to a belief in its existence.

One way out seems to be by recognizing that any faith in scientific inferences *require* faith in the continuity of the world. Tomorrow will be very much like today. This does not prove that nature never takes leaps; it is only indirectly related to this issue. Indeed she may; or she may apparently leap—only to let man find that the leap occurs under knowable conditions and hence is no leap at all: the leap in concept formation may be relatively orderly.

Consider what life would be like if we did not assume that the universe is orderly: if the future is not like the past—if nature is not ordered by the same laws as before—what will it be like?

I must admit that a probability of zero does not warrant the inference that the event in question is impossible. Possibility is a matter of theory. We cannot equate things that are imaginable with things that are possible. Although one is perfectly capable of imagining the sun's blowing up tomorrow, our theory asserts that this is impossible. Now let us deny our theory, and allow all imaginable alternatives to be possible. Now, what will tomorrow be like? Just for fun, allow some trivial modifications: tomorrow I will have purple skin with yellow dots; or yellow skin with purple dots; or no skin at all, or orange bark, or— the writer, the printer, and the reader must tire easily of the various alternatives. Indeed, there must be at least a denumerable infinity of them.

In the face of an infinite number of alternatives, which should we plan on? Since we have rejected theory, each must be equally likely. The highly imaginative person can conceive of many more than the dull or catatonic person. But neither the dull nor the catatonic have shown a mastery of the world. The point is simple: if every imaginable alternative to this world is equally likely, there is no way to decide how to act. Only if we are able to expect that what was true in the past will be true in the future can we plan.

Thus, although science proves nothing, in any final sense of proof, until we fail, we must accept what science has shown to be consistent with its postulates and definitions. If we are to bridge the gap between the past and the future, we must act as though science has proved its point. It is the only sensible thing to do. I leave it to the reader to define sensible.

NOTES, APPENDIX, AND INDEX

NOTES

Chapter 1. Introduction

[1] Roy G. Francis, "Science and Prediction," *Midwest Sociologist*, No. 2, Spring 1956, pp. 7–12.

[2] John T. Doby, et al., *Introduction to Social Research* (Harrisburg, Pa.: Stackpole Co., 1954), esp. pp. 3–19.

[3] Felix Kaufmann, *Methodology of the Social Sciences* (New York: Oxford University Press, 1944), pp. 48–76.

[4] Paul F. Lazarsfeld, Foreword to *Experimental Sociology* by Ernest Greenwood (New York: King's Crown Press, 1945), p. vii.

[5] For a specific criticism of extreme operationalism, see Harold Orbach, "Operational Definitions and the Natural Science Trend," *Midwest Sociologist*, 19, No. 2, May 1957, pp. 101–103.

[6] George A. Lundberg, "The Natural Science Trend in Sociology," *American Journal of Sociology*, 61, November 1955, pp. 191–202.

[7] Roy G. Francis, *Mathematical Analysis of Birth Order Data*, University of Minnesota Experiment Station, Technical Bulletin 216, July 1955.

[8] John H. Kolb, *Rural Primary Groups*, Agricultural Experiment Station Research Bulletin 51, 1921. The central device was the recognition of a place-name. The significance of names was not, apparently, well understood on either side of the argument.

Chapter 2. Categorical Logic

[1] Kaufmann, *op. cit.*, pp. 50–51.

Chapter 3. Problems in the Proof of Causality

[1] David Hume, *An Enquiry Concerning the Human Understanding, and An Enquiry Concerning the Principles of Morals* (Oxford: Clarendon Press, 1894), p. 24.

[2] *Ibid.*, note 4.

[3] *Ibid.*, pp. 25–26.

[4] *Ibid.*, pp. 44–45.

[5] *Ibid.*, p. 63.

[6] Karl Pearson, *The Grammar of Science* (London: Adam and Charles Black, 1911), pp. 170–171.

[7] Howard Becker, *Through Values to Social Interpretation* (Durham, N.C.: Duke University Press, 1950), p. 99. Chapter 2 of Harry E. Barnes, Howard Becker, and Frances Becker's *Contemporary Social Theory* (New York: Appleton-Century, 1940) contains much of Becker's argument on ideal and constructed types.

[8] Morris R. Cohen and Ernest Nagel, *An Introduction to Logic and Scientific Method* (New York: Harcourt, Brace & Company, War Dept. Education Manual,

EM 621, 1934), especially Chapter 13, "The Methods of Experimental Inquiry." All references to Mill come from this chapter; they cite his *A System of Logic*. It is interesting to note, incidentally, that the 1904 Harper edition of Mill's *System of Logic* uses the phrase "an indispensable part" in the definition of the method of difference, where the 1869 edition had said "a necessary part." The change in terminology could be accounted for by the identification of "cause" with "logical necessity," an identification at least insinuated in the first edition. Whether "an indispensable part" is a proper escape can be doubted, for one would be tempted to ask just what an indispensable part is; if it should turn out that an indispensable part is either a cause or a part of the cause, one would feel trapped in a circular argument.

[9] Bertrand Russell, *An Introduction to Mathematical Philosophy* (London: George Allen & Unwin, Ltd., 1948), p. 27.

[10] Florian Znaniecki, *The Method of Sociology* (New York: Farrar & Rinehart, Inc., 1934).

[11] *Ibid.*, p. 239.

[12] *Ibid.*, p. 249.

[13] *Ibid.*

[14] Howard Becker, *German Youth: Bond or Free?* (New York: Oxford University Press, 1947). Although Becker has used his cultural case-study method, especially as it involves an argument on the type level, he has not, to my knowledge, claimed that this kind of argument presents an unequivocal and finally certain proof.

[15] William S. Robinson, "The Logical Structure of Analytic Induction," *American Sociological Review*, Vol. 16, No. 6, December 1951, pp. 812–818. Robinson draws upon Donald R. Cressey's dissertation, "Criminal Violation of Financial Trust," Indiana University, 1950. Cressey published a similarly titled paper in the *American Sociological Review* (Vol. K, No. 6, December 1950, pp. 738–743). No systematic development of analytic induction is offered; only in a general footnote on method does he include a reference to Znaniecki's *The Method of Sociology*. Allusions to the reformulation of the hypothesis and "the final hypothesis in its complete form" (p. 743) suggest his use of the method.

[16] Znaniecki, *op. cit.*, p. 225.

[17] R. A. Fisher, *The Design of Experiments* (New York: Hafner Publishing Co., Inc., 1949), pp. 7–8.

[18] Margaret Hagood and Daniel O. Price, *Statistics for Sociologists* (New York: Henry Holt & Company, 1952), p. 190.

[19] Roy G. Francis and Cornelius Golightly," "On Scientific Inference," *Midwest Sociologist*, Vol. 17, No. 1, Winter 1955, p. 30.

[20] F. J. Teggart, compiler, *The Idea of Progress* (Berkeley: University of California Press, 1949), p. 204.

[21] "Scientifically, only to the extent that an inquiry can be replicated can there be empirical prediction. And this implies that the classes of both the problematic and explanatory data must in fact recur." Francis, "Science and Prediction," p. 12.

Chapter 4. The Rejection of Chance

[1] J. V. Uspensky, *Introduction to Mathematical Probability* (New York: McGraw-Hill Book Company, Inc., 1937), p. 6.

[2] Richard von Mises, *Probability, Statistics and Truth* (New York: Macmillan Company, 1939) and lecture notes from his class in mathematical probability in the fall semester of 1952 at Harvard. One of the better discussions of von Mises, presented with the intention of criticizing the frequency theory, is that of William Kneale in *Probability and Induction* (London: Oxford University Press, 1952, corrected sheets of the first edition), especially pp. 152ff. It is interesting to note that von Mises used to discuss philosophers in a satiric manner while he was presenting

NOTES

his own philosophical point of view. This is, I suspect, a technique the positivist who was busily overthrowing metaphysics happily employed. It made, I must admit, good listening.

³ With the exception of an unimaginative possibility of having a sampling procedure of this kind: take only zeros, returning everything else.

⁴ William Feller, *An Introduction to Probability Theory and Its Applications*, Vol. 1 (New York: John Wiley & Sons, Inc., 1950), p. 6.

⁵ This is the conclusion reached also by M. G. Kendall in "Reconcilation of Theories of Probability," *Biometrika*, 36, June 1949, p. 103. I acknowledge my indebtedness to Kendall. One of the most rigorous statements of the analysis of categorically classified data is found in the first five chapters of *An Introduction to the Theory of Statistics* by G. Udny Yule and M. G. Kendall. This book has been revised a number of times; I am best acquainted with the eleventh edition (London: Charles Griffin & Co., Ltd., 1937). Any reader who is not aware of this volume would be well advised to correct what would appear to most statisticians an obvious deficiency.

⁶ Paul G. Hoel, *Introduction to Mathematical Statistics* (New York: John Wiley & Sons, Inc., 1947), pp. 172–174.

⁷ Francis and Golightly, *op. cit.*

⁸ Thomas C. McCormick, *Elementary Social Statistics* (New York: McGraw-Hill Book Company, 1941), p. 144.

⁹ Major P. A. Macmahon, *An Introduction to Combinatory Analysis* (Cambridge: Cambridge University Press, 1920), p. 8. This small book gives a fairly complete discussion of combinations and permutations. The analytic distinction between the presence or absence of order is basic to an understanding of combinatory analysis.

¹⁰ R. A. Fisher, *Statistical Methods for Research Workers* (Oliver & Boyd, Ltd., 1941), pp. 94–97.

¹¹ Two articles appeared in *Biometrika*, Vol. 36, 1947, on these problems. One was "Significance Tests for 2 x 2 Tables," by G. A. Barnard (pp. 123–138). The other was "The Choice of Statistical Tests Illustrated on the Interpretation of Data Classed in a 2 x 2 Table," by E. S. Pearson (pp. 139–167). The two give very nearly identical results, as Barnard comments in a brief statement, "2 x 2 Tables" (pp. 168–169).

¹² George Snedecor, *Statistical Methods: Applied to Experiments in Agriculture and Biology* (Ames: Iowa State College Press, 1946), p. 22.

¹³ R. A. Fisher and F. Yates, *Statistical Tables for Biological, Agricultural, and Medical Research* (Edinburgh: Oliver and Boyd, Ltd., 1938), p. 3.

¹⁴ Hoel argues that the expected frequency should be greater than 5 and so should the degrees of freedom, but that the former is a more stringent argument (*op. cit.*, p. 191). Quinn McNemar, in his *Psychological Statistics* (New York: John Wiley & Sons, Inc., 2nd ed., 1955, p. 222), holds merely to the restriction that the expected frequency should be greater than 5, if one is cautious in interpreting the result.

Chapter 5. Alternatives to Chance

¹ Or words to that effect. The phraseology has become so common that to cite any example would be misleading and would bring all sorts of charges against the point I am trying to make. Rather than quote examples and then defend myself against charges of unfairly criticizing a particular article or quoting out of context, or suggest that those whose passages were cited peculiarly guilty, only obvious paraphrases will be used. The usage is so common that no citation is needed to prove its existence. The reader who has never encountered the phrase need only pick up a current issue of practically any journal of the social sciences. If the article contains any statistical test at all, the odds are that the author will calmly assert that he will test the

null hypothesis. Or he will say that he will put his hypothesis into the null form, as though the alternatives truly are contradictions. Of course he will test the null hypothesis. We all do.

[2] In this case, one would have to minimize type II error. A discussion of that argument is beyond the scope of the treatment here.

[3] The point at issue is admittedly subtle and could require considerable attention for its discernment. For those who have had no formal training in logic, a review of Chapter 2's discussion of elementary logic may clarify the way I am trying to develop the point.

[4] At the .05 level, with large samples.

[5] The example is taken from Roy G. Francis and Robert C. Stone, *Service and Procedure in Bureaucracy* (Minneapolis: University of Minnesota Press, 1956). I will have to be sketchy in my development here. Moreover, for references to the original ideas, the reader should refer to the works cited in that volume. The purpose now is to illustrate an argument, not to prove a theoretical point; thus, the present case does not require the truth of any proposition to be asserted.

Chapter 6. Other Measures of Association

[1] McCormick, *Elementary Social Statistics*, p. 213.

[2] Leo A. Goodman and William H. Kruskal, "Measures of Association for Cross Classification," *Journal of the American Statistical Association*, 49, December 1954, pp. 732ff.

[3] Francis, "Science and Prediction," p. 12.

[4] Julius A. Jahn, "The Measurement of Ecological Segregation," *American Sociological Review*, 15, No. 1, February 1950, pp. 100–104. Jahn points out how similar this index is to Guttman's index of predictability, discussed in *The Prediction of Personal Adjustment*, Social Science Research Council Bulletin No. 48, pp. 258–263. Although Jahn makes much of a word borrowed from Guttman—reproducibility—he correctly points out that he has a completely different derivation and interpretation of the formula.

[5] Jahn, *op. cit.*, p. 103.

Chapter 7. An Attempt to Measure Causality

[1] As William P. Davey has pointed out in private correspondence, the use of "because" in explaining things is very common, even among those who deplore causal explanations.

[2] Thomas C. McCormick, "Toward Causal Analysis in the Prediction of Attributes," *American Sociological Review*, Vol. 17, No. 1, February 1952, pp. 35–44.

[3] *Ibid.*, p. 35.

[4] McCormick, *Elementary Social Statistics*, pp. 222–223.

[5] McCormick, "Toward Causal Analysis," p. 36; italics mine.

[6] *Ibid.*, p. 35.

[7] *Ibid.*, p. 38.

[8] *Ibid.*, p. 36.

[9] *Loc. cit.*

[10] *Ibid.*, p. 39.

[11] McCormick goes on to suggest comparison of two or more causal systems and the accumulation of a record of success in order that the table may be "revised." These are not relevant to the problem before us, that of measuring causality; hence they will not be fully discussed.

[12] McCormick reports a three-by-three table. However, Lancaster has shown that any r x s table "may be reduced to $(r-1)(s-1)$ two-by-two tables; the value of

χ^2 for each table will be independent of the other tables; these will be summed to give χ^2 for $(r-1)(s-1)$ degrees of freedom." H. O. Lancaster, "Partition of χ^2 in Certain Discrete Distributions" (*Biometrika*, 36, June 1949, p. 120). Although we shall not determine the χ^2 for the table McCormick reports, we are justified in discussing a particular two-by-two table. This will necessarily result in numerical differences from the cited example.

[13] McCormick, "Toward Causal Analysis," p. 37.

[14] *Ibid.*, p. 40; the original text refers to table numbers in the article; I have adjusted these.

[15] *Ibid.*, p. 39; "If, as is proper in a causal table, it is desired to achieve a sufficient cause for each row, the table must of course be square." And again, pp. 39–40, he writes, "The table or subtable of attributes that is not square has no meaning in causal analysis."

[16] *Ibid.*, p. 39.

[17] *Ibid.*

[18] *Ibid.*

Chapter 8. Correlated Dichotomies and the Problem of Joint Effects

[1] This idea of a "type" is rather simple. For some sophisticated discussions, although from different points of view, see Roy G. Francis and Don Martindale, "The Scientific Status of Mathematical Models and Ideal Types as Illustrated in Demographic Research" (*Alpha Kappa Deltan*, 25, No. 3, Spring 1955); Paul F. Lazarsfeld, "Some Remarks on the Typological Procedures in Social Research," *Zeitschrift für Sozialforschung*, 6, June 1937, pp. 119–139; and John C. McKinney, "Constructive Typology and Social Research," in Doby *et al.*, *op. cit.*, pp. 139–195.

[2] Francis and Stone, *op. cit.*

[3] Benjamin W. White and Eli Saltz, "Measurement of Reproducibility," *Psychological Bulletin*, 54, No. 2, 1957, pp. 81–99. Because of the criticisms leveled at the Guttman scale by Francis and Stone ("Measurement and Attitude Analysis," *Midwest Sociologist*, 18, No. 1, pp. 6–26), I will not discuss that scale here. Two points may be offered, however. First, the Guttman scale does not warrant the inference of unidimensionality. Second, reproducibility need not be fixed to any idea of scaling. A measure of the height of a person does not allow one to reproduce the size of the trunk, thorax, or any other part of the body, the sum of which would give the total height. Hence, the Guttman scale *cannot* be regarded as the *ideal* scale.

[4] I wish to thank the late David Shaw for calling my attention to the paper upon which this section is largely based. Indeed, he assisted with some of the algebra and suggested some of the symbols used. The paper is "A Generalization of Analysis of Variance and Multivariate Analysis to Data Based on Frequencies in Qualitative Categories or Class Intervals," S. N. Roy and Marvin A. Kastenbaum, Institute of Statistics, Mimeograph Series No. 131, June 1, 1955. The interpretation is mine, however, and I alone am responsible for any errors that may appear. For any derivation, the reader is referred to the cited paper.

[5] In some places, the term employed is "interaction." However, it occurs to me that interaction already has a good theoretical meaning in most of the social sciences. Rather than confuse the two—for the meanings are vastly different—I resurrect the older term, "joint effects."

[6] See, for example, Paul R. Rider, *College Algebra* (New York: Macmillan Company, 1955), pp. 230–232.

[7] *Ibid.*

[8] The technique for computing square root is bad enough; a good motive for learning logarithms could well be to avoid the pains of extracting higher roots.

THE RHETORIC OF SCIENCE

Chapter 9. Summary and Conclusions

[1] See Robert MacIver, *Social Causation* (Boston: Ginn and Company, 1942). Here the significance of using the word "why" rather than the word "how" may be thrust upon the reader. Unfortunately, the word "why" has been assigned to philosophy and theology. It can, however, be sensibly used in other places; "Why are two and two four?" is less cumbersome than any usage with "how." To a great many people, "why" connotes ultimates, and so becomes taboo in modern scientific usage.

[2] While most translate *cogito* "I think" rather than "I doubt," the use of "I doubt" lends itself to the mood of science better than does "I think."

[3] Doby, *et al.*, *op. cit.* However, "analysis" was not distinguished as a separate activity of science. I am not happy with that term, and use it under protest.

APPENDIX

The Logs of n! for n = 1 to n = 100

n	log n!	n	log n!	n	log n!	n	log n!
1	0.00000	26	26.60562	51	66.19064	76	111.27543
2	0.30103	27	28.03698	52	67.90665	77	113.16192
3	0.77815	28	29.41249	53	69.63092	78	115.05401
4	1.38021	29	30.94654	54	71.36332	79	116.95164
5	2.07918	30	32.42366	55	73.10368	80	118.85473
6	2.85733	31	33.91502	56	74.85187	81	120.76321
7	3.70243	32	35.42017	57	76.60774	82	122.67703
8	4.60552	33	36.93869	58	78.37117	83	124.59610
9	5.55976	34	38.47016	59	80.14202	84	126.52038
10	6.55976	35	40.01423	60	81.92017	85	128.44980
11	7.60116	36	41.57054	61	83.70550	86	130.38430
12	8.68034	37	43.13874	62	85.49790	87	132.32382
13	9.79428	38	44.71852	63	87.29724	88	134.26830
14	10.94041	39	46.30959	64	89.10342	89	136.21769
15	12.11650	40	47.91165	65	90.91633	90	138.17194
16	13.32062	41	49.52443	66	92.73587	91	140.13098
17	14.55107	42	51.14768	67	94.56195	92	142.09476
18	15.80634	43	52.78115	68	96.39446	93	144.06325
19	17.08509	44	54.42460	69	98.23331	94	146.03638
20	18.38612	45	56.07781	70	100.07840	95	148.01410
21	19.70834	46	57.74057	71	101.92966	96	149.99637
22	21.05077	47	59.41267	72	103.78700	97	151.98314
23	22.41249	48	61.09391	73	105.65032	98	153.97437
24	23.79271	49	62.78410	74	107.51955	99	155.97000
25	25.19065	50	64.48307	75	109.39461	100	157.97000

INDEX

A or not A, 12, 59
Agreement, Mill's canon of, 53
Alternative, strong, as syllogism, 33
Alternatives to chance, 86; relations to logical forms, 91–93
Analysis, 160, 167; and ethical neutrality, 161; and practical activity, 161
Analytical classification, 12
Analytical induction, 45–48
Applied science, control of variables, 161
Approximation, degrees of, 97
Aristotelian logic, 13, 20, 120
Association, 41, 42, 156; and criticism of Karl Pearson, 43; measures of, 164 ff

Barnard, B. A., 77, 175n
Barnes, H. E., 173n
Becker, Howard, 42, 46, 173n, 174n
Behavior of men, 4; science as, 7, 9
Belief and knowledge, 4
Bernoulli, Daniel, 63

Categorical logic, 13, 16
Causal explanation, 120
Causal monism, 37, 45, 82
Causal pluralism, 36
Causal relation, 156
Causality, 15; proof of, 36
Causation: multiple, 36; Mill's canon of, 43
Cause: first, 37–38; and necessity, 38; denial of, with linear correlations, 42; historical error in its search, 54; as relation, 54, 122, 156; proving, 120; chance and, 123; estimating amount of, 123; simple measure of, 124; and prediction, 126; and certainty, 127; a primitive concept, 127, 155; plural, 131
Chance: rejection of, 62; distribution, 128
Cheshire, L., 113, 114
Chi-square, 77, 163–64; distribution of, 78; formula for, 79; short-cut formula, 79–

81, 164; corrected for continuity, 84; and critical ratio, 90–91; illustrated, 128; faulty example of, 139–40; correlation proportions, 139, 140–42, 142-43, 164; Yates' correction for, 164
Cohen, M. R., 43, 44, 45, 173n
Combinations, 72, 73
Conceptual definitions, 13
Concomitant variation, Mill's method of, 44
Contingency, coefficient of, 104, 166; example, 106; formula, 106; correction for, 106, 107; compared to Yule's Q, 108
Continuity, law of, 51
Contradiction: law of, 20, 101; relation between propositions, 27
Contrariety, 26; simple, 27; weak, 101
Convergence, 11
Conviction, an emotional state, 16
Copulated class, 21, 22, 24, 28, 29
Correctness of decision, 16

Davey, W. P., 120, 176n
Decision regarding propositions, 8
Demonstration as intellectual process, 16
Descartes, René, 158
Dichotomy, 12, 13; rule for, 102
Difference, Mill's method of, 43–44
Disjunctive syllogism, 33
Doby, J. T., 7, 159, 173n, 178n
Doubt, location of, 159

Einstein, Albert, 49
Empirical research, ends of, 51
Equivalence, 24
Error, in measurement, 12; and operational specifications, 12, 122, 155; Type II, 49; Type I, 49, 50, 78
Ethical neutrality and analysis, 161
Event with more than one outcome, 12
Excluded middle, law of, 20

180

INDEX

THE RHETORIC OF SCIENCE

INDEX

Two-by-two table, 15, 21, 22, 47, 59, 90, 162; as heuristic device, 135; for scale construction, 145; and logical relations, 157

Type I error, 49, 50, 78

Type II error, 49

Universal affirmative, 21

Universal negative, 21

Uspensky, J. V., 64, 73, 174n

von Mises, Richard, 64, 65, 66, 174n

White, B. W., 143, 177n

Yates, F., 84, 175n

Yates' correction, 164

Yule, G. U., 15, 175n

Yule's Q, 104, 166; example, 105; formula, 105; compared with coefficient of contingency, 108; tetrachoric correlation, 112; lambda b, and Jahn's index of segregation, 119; kappa-prime, 125–34, 165

Znaniecki, Florian, 45, 46, 174n